# Contents

P9-CPY-372

# THE ISSUES COLLECTION

## COLLECTION EDITOR:
## GILLDA LEITENBERG

## Global Issues

### EDITED BY SHELLY BRYAN

◆ ◆ ◆

To Robert and Sheila Bryan
whose love and support have
helped me always

McGraw-Hill Ryerson Limited

Toronto • Montreal • New York • Auckland • Bogotá
Caracas • Lisbon • London • Madrid • Mexico • Milan
New Delhi • Paris • San Juan • Singapore • Sydney • Tokyo

**Global Issues**
**The Issues Collection**

Copyright © McGraw-Hill Ryerson Limited, 1993
All rights reserved. No part of this publication may be reproduced or transmitted in any
form or by any means, or stored in a data base or retrieval system, without the prior
written permission of McGraw-Hill Ryerson Limited.

ISBN 0-07-551446-X

2 3 4 5 6 7 8 9 10  BG  2 1 0 9 8 7 6 5 4

Printed and bound in Canada

**Canadian Cataloguing in Publication Data**
Main entry under title:

Global Issues

(The Issues collection)
For use in grades 7, 8, 9.
ISBN 0-07-551446-X

1. Readers (Elementary). 2. Readers (Secondary).
3. International relations — Literary collections.
4. World politics — Literary collections.
I. Bryan, Shelly. II. Series.

PE1121.G56 1993    808'.0427    C92-095796-X

Editor: *Kathy Evans*
Senior Supervising Editor: *Carol Altilia*
Permissions Editor: *Jacqueline Russell*
Designer: *Mary Opper*
Typesetter: *Pages Design Ltd.*
Photo Researcher: *Elaine Freedman*
Cover Illustrator: *Jamie Bennet*

This book was manufactured in Canada using acid-free and recycled paper.

# Introduction

*This book is all about global issues. You will read about issues facing people all over the world and, as you react to, and interact with, the selections, I hope you will begin to grow as a responsible world citizen.*

*I hope your growth will be noticeable through an increasing awareness of how people everywhere are dealing with changes in their world. You might become more empathetic to the situations facing others and will probably begin to re-examine the way you interact with others and the world around you. You will learn that issues are complex and that there are many perspectives from which to approach them. Most of all, I hope you will become more aware of the ways you can have a positive impact on the world by "thinking globally when acting locally."*

*Global issues, as you will discover in your reading, are complex and far-reaching. You'll read about the world as a "global village"; environmental problems and the work being done to solve them; economic and political relationships among countries; issues such as hunger, poverty, illiteracy; human rights and peace. The issues are serious, but, ultimately, they will be manageable. You have a big responsibility — you are in charge of tomorrow. You will be the decision makers. Happily for all of us, your generation has already demonstrated an awareness of and concern for many of these issues. Many individuals and schools have already responded and are taking steps toward improvement in creative and exciting ways.*

*The ultimate goal of this or any other book is to somehow enrich your life. I hope that this book will do so, and also that it will help you adapt to a rapidly changing world. This book is about change and, in this instance, a change for the better.*

*Shelly Bryan*

# Space
# Gives Us
# a Global
# Perspective

◆ ◆ ◆

**BY**

**WENDY WARREN**

**KEEBLER**

**L**et's start with wheels. The Pontiac LeMans is an American car. It has a French name; it was designed in Germany; it is built in Korea; it travels on U.S. and Canadian highways.

The Mars Rover is a Russian robotic vehicle. It has an English name and a Russian name (Marsokhod); it was designed and built in Russia; it will be tested by Russians, Americans and Europeans at Death Valley, Calif.; it will travel on the Martian surface.

Confused? Don't be. It all makes perfect sense in a global economy and a new world order.

It's logical to look at space — and space science — for a global perspective. Looking back at the Earth from "out there" provides a clearer picture of shifting or vanishing borders.

"The whole planet, everything from the entertainment industry to financial services to commerce, is becoming more global — politics aside," says Harvey Meyerson, president of the U.S. International Space Year Association in Washington, D.C. "So it's only natural that space is perceived as kind of a symbol of all this. It's only from space that we have really begun to perceive the planet as a whole."

Roberta Bondar, the Canadian astronaut who spent eight days in space in January 1992 aboard the space shuttle Discovery, has also expressed this view.

"You only have to look out a couple of degrees from the surface of the Earth," she told a group of students in Ottawa, "and all you see is the black void of the universe, the cold vacuum of space."

"And then you look back down to the Earth, bathed in sunlight...and it makes you feel very proud to be not only Canadian but to be from this planet."

"My message to you today is to cherish this planet."

It's no accident that this [1992] has been declared International Space Year in 30 countries. It's the 500th anniversary of Columbus' voyage. It's the 35th anniversary of Sputnik, the first of many voyages in the direction of new worlds. And it's the first year the two superpowers — the United States and the former Soviet Union — are not arch rivals in a space race.

"The days of nationalistic pride are over, submerged to the idea that we ought to be working with other nations."

So says Louis Friedman, executive director of the Planetary Society, a group based in Pasadena, Calif., whose 100 000 members from 100 countries contributed $200 000 towards the Mars Rover project. This spirit is widespread among space scientists and administrators, not to mention heads of state.

This is also a time of economic pressure, and the idea of pooling resources and scientific talent is attractive to space agencies of many nations. The National Aeronautics and Space Administration is an old hand at this.

"NASA has co-operated internationally for over 30 years. We have a long history of doing that," says Lynne Cline, NASA's deputy director of international relations.

The January mission of Discovery is an example. As well as Bondar, a neurologist from Sault Ste. Marie, the crew included German physicist Ulf Merbold. More than 225 scientists from 14 countries were involved in the mission's medical and scientific experiments.

What's new seems to be the pace and scope of international co-operation in space. Many countries are more involved in other countries' missions. U.S. instruments are flying on Japanese and Russian spacecraft. The international space station Freedom will have labs provided by the United States, Europe, Japan and Canada.

"Co-operation has been increasing, getting more complex, involving more countries," Cline says. "There are obviously benefits."

The international space perspective comes into clearest focus with a program called Mission to Planet Earth. This is the theme of a series of space projects using unstaffed satellites to take measurements of the Earth's atmosphere, to look at the oceans and land masses, to see, as Cline puts it, "what space can contribute to understanding how the Earth works as a system."

Countries will work together to monitor and protect the Earth's environment, to study problems such as pollution, global warming and deforestation.

"Those problems don't know national boundaries," says University of Michigan space sciences professor Sushil Atreya. "We should all be solving them together. We all have a stake in it."

Plainly and simply, it's cheaper to go together. Says Cline: "Putting together the resources of two or more countries allows you to do a larger project or do it sooner."

The Russian Mars Rover project got a big boost from the $200 000 raised by the Planetary Society. That may not seem like a huge amount of money, but "it's a big deal to them," Friedman says. With Russia's rampant inflation, he says, $1000 is practically one human-year of effort in Russia. "That's a lot of talent you buy for $1000 that you can't do any other way."

This was privately raised money, of course. NASA itself does not provide funds for space programs in other countries. "NASA has used that rule consistently throughout its space program. We don't have authorization to do foreign aid," Cline says.

Instead, NASA shares the work with space agencies in other countries. An example is the Cassini project, an unstaffed mission planned for launch to Saturn's moon Titan in 1997. NASA is building the orbiter, and the European Space Agency is building the probe. It works out to a $400-million expenditure for Europe, $1.4 billion for the United States.

Sometimes, when so many parties are involved, co-operation can be a problem. For example, when part of the Russian Mars mission was delayed by two years, NASA's original plans to help relay data from its own orbiting Mars Observer became uncertain.

Science by definition requires dialogue and sharing. "We don't have a monopoly on good ideas or good technology," says Friedman.

# The Thread

◆ ◆ ◆

**BY**

**TOM**

**WAYMAN**

A loose thread at my shirt cuff.
I pull
and it unwinds around my sleeve.
As I tug, I glance ahead
to guess how far it will unravel.
In the distance, I observe the thread leading
to the machine of a woman in Seoul
who assembled my garment. I hear her voice
above the noise of the factory:
*Most people in this district*
*act as if it is our destiny to be poor.*
*But is that right? We work from seven in the morning*
*until eleven-thirty in the evening. Our skin turns color*
*because of less chance to be outside.*
*Also my hands have many wounds*
*from the sewing. And sometimes I can't open my eyes*
*in strong sunlight. I don't know the name*
*of that disease.*

From the bobbin she touches
the thread unrolls eastward
to the cotton plants of a man in Texas.
If I kneel where his tractor pulls a plow
through the rich soil
I can see where the thread starts.

A foot or so below the surface
the thread joins the top of a ball of twine
enormous as the planet. If I place my fingers and palm
on this tightly-wound sphere
I can feel its vibrating hum.

I reach the same destination
when my thick fingers take hold of some matter
caught between my teeth. I yank
and what pulls free
is the beginning of a great looping wire
generated by supermarket clerks, long-haul drivers,
stoop harvesters, seed merchants
that also extends back to the earth.

This is why I am certain
what passes through our lives
inextricably links us with each other.
And that nothing we encounter is ours alone.
There is no way to sever,
to possess a portion of twine.
Men and women can use a length of cable
for a whip or noose. They can pollute a section
with poison or slime. Yet these debased bits of string
do not belong to them completely
despite their bragging.

Moments after each of us is born
the umbilical cord is cut.
But other fibres that tie us to our parents
commence at once to stretch
into bands that feed us and join us to the rest of the room
and beyond. We remain enmeshed our entire lives,
pulling the net this direction and that
as we travel and age, the web that holds us
flexible enough to let some of us journey to the moon.
Yet the anchor
of each of the million cords that wrap me,
that connect me to justice and injustice,
remains that closely-wound, pulsing ball
of global string.

Even these words
were handed to me
containing the grammars and syntaxes
others built and tore down
and constructed again, new verbs
forming, and nouns
appearing in my mouth or from under my pen:
airborne seeds from elsewhere
that find root in my days
— some destructive, some helpful,
each word trailing a resilient tendril,
another thread
that weaves me and all I do
into the warp of our world.

# This Day in History

♦ ♦ ♦

**BY**

**BERT**

**ALMON**

The radio tells me
that back in 1950
the sun rose blue
over Great Britain,
from forest fires
in Western Canada.
I know the dust of
exploding Krakatoa
gave the whole world
a year of fine sunsets.

I try to imagine
whose labor I lift
on my fork, what
ashes sift in my tea,
and get about as far
as the corner market.
We can say "brother"
to everyone, but
only a blue sunrise
might make us feel it.

# How Many Passengers on Our Planet?

◆ ◆ ◆

**BY**

**LAURENCE PRINGLE**

**P**ick up a handful of soil anywhere on earth. In it you will find more organisms — visible and microscopic — than exist on the entire surfaces of other planets.

The planet Mars is icy cold — and lifeless. The planet Venus is fiery hot — and lifeless. Between these planets lies our home, Earth. Its atmosphere makes it an oasis in space, with a favorable climate, abundant water, and a rich variety of living things.

Scientists are dazzled and puzzled by the diversity of life on earth. No one knows how many different kinds of plants, animals, and other organisms there are. But we do know that the organisms identified so far are only a small fraction of all living things. There are millions — perhaps many millions — that await discovery.

The study of living things is called biology (*bio* is a Greek term for "life"). Scientists who study living things are called biologists. And biologists have a name for the earth's incredible variety of life: biodiversity.

The first step toward understanding this biodiversity is naming and describing the different living organisms. Throughout human history and all over the world, people have given names to animals and plants they recognize. For example, in New Guinea, hunters can name sixteen different frogs, seventeen lizards and snakes, more than a hundred birds, and many more insects and worms. The New Guinea hunters are walking encyclopedias of information about the life around them.

Besides naming things, people have tried to make sense of the earth's biodiversity by considering similar organisms to be members of groups. The modern system of naming and classifying living things was devised by Swedish botanist Carl von Linné (Carolus Linnaeus) in the eighteenth century. At that time,

Linné and other scientists believed that perhaps 50 000 kinds of organisms lived on earth.

Since then, more than 1.5 million kinds, or species, have been discovered and named. They include 250 000 species of flowering plants and 41 000 kinds of vertebrate animals. These animals with backbones include about 4000 mammals, 19 000 fishes, about 9000 birds, and more than 10 000 reptiles and amphibians. The largest group by far is the insects, with more than 751 000 named so far. The remainder includes worms, spiders, fungi, algae, and microorganisms.

Biologists believe that most of the earth's flowering plants and vertebrate animals have been discovered. They estimate that only a few thousand more fishes, birds, reptiles, and other vertebrates are likely to be found. The greatest riches of biodiversity remain to be discovered in the world of insects and other small creatures without backbones (invertebrates).

Biologists expect to find some of the earth's undescribed organisms living in coral reefs. There also may be other undiscovered habitats, and species, on the floor of the deep ocean. In the 1980s, using small research submarines, scientists began to discover new forms of life — crabs, fishes, shrimps, tube worms — near geysers of hot, mineral-laden water that spew from the ocean floor.

The earth's greatest riches, however, lie in tropical rain forests. In the 1980s, as funds for tropical research increased, biologists found astonishing numbers of animals there.

In Panama, entomologist Terry Erwin of the Smithsonian Institution collected insects from nineteen trees of the same species. On those trees alone, he found more than 12 000 different kinds of beetles. He estimated that one out of seven species lived on that kind of tree and no other.

Erwin also collected insects from one tree in the Amazon rain forest of Peru. He sent the ant specimens to be identified by biologist Edward O. Wilson of Harvard University. Wilson found forty-three kinds of ants, including several new species. This diversity of ants — from a single tropical tree — equaled the number of ant species that are known to live in all of Canada or Great Britain.

Tropical forests are also rich with plant life. In Borneo, a botanist discovered 700 species of trees growing on ten separate plots of land that totaled about twenty-five acres. This matches the number of tree species growing in all of North America. Also, the trunks and branches of rain forest trees are habitats for mosses, ferns, lichens, orchids, and other plants that grow far above the soil. In Costa Rica alone, more than 1100 species of orchids have been identified.

In the 1980s, Terry Erwin and other biologists began for the first time to study insects, plants, and other organisms that live near the tops of tropical trees. The organisms living in the treetops, or canopy, of a rain forest are different from those living on or close to the ground. More than half of all rain forest species may live aloft. Most of them never touch the ground. Terry Erwin has called the tropical forest canopy "the heart" of the earth's biodiversity.

Until the 1980s, biologists estimated that 3 to 5 million species live on earth. However, since large numbers of tropical insects and other organisms may live on just one kind of tree, or in one small area of tropical forest, the biodiversity of earth may be much greater. Terry Erwin has estimated that the earth may be home to 30 million species of insects alone.

The total of all kinds of life could be much higher. Rain forest canopies harbor not only insects but also unknown numbers of mites, roundworms, fungi, and other small organisms. Little is known about life in tropical soils. And most animals have other living things, called parasites, living on or inside them.

Whether the total number of species is 5 million, 30 million, or more, we know very little about the biodiversity of our planet. Our ignorance is great.

Suppose the number of species is "only" 10 million. This means that we have perhaps discovered just 15 percent of the total number of species. Then consider that we have not yet learned much about the plants and animals that *have* been identified. Many of these organisms are "known" only in the sense that a few individuals are kept as preserved specimens in scientific collections and that they have been given a formal name.

Their lives are a mystery. Their links with other living things, their importance in nature, and their possible value to humans are also mysteries.

# Inherit the Earth

◆ ◆ ◆

BY

LYNN

MOORE

**A**s we slide headlong toward the 21st century, our planet is awash with pollution. Its inhabitants mistreat their fellow humans and abuse the creatures they call lesser animals.

Ask teenagers about this sorry state of affairs and chances are they will rap out a litany of new-age complaints previously unknown to the older generation who can remember when the buzzword was simply "peace" not "Greenpeace."

But — if *The Gazette's* panel of Young Montrealers is any indication — today's teenagers do more than talk about the problems that plague them and their parents. They are working to be part of the solution.

When the 15 Young Montrealers met to discuss social concerns, they also talked about what they were doing to make the world a better place. No limit had been put on the topics; the teens were simply asked to tell us what they felt should matter more to our society and be taken more seriously by everyone. (For the record the Meech Lake accord did not make anyone's list.)

The No.1 concern voiced by most of the panelists was the environment.

"The reason I chose the environment is that unless we do something about the environment now, we won't have to worry about poverty or cruelty to animals or education because there probably won't be anything at the rate our environment is going," said Anjum Hanafi, a 15-year-old student at the Sacred Heart School.

While the environment was foremost, several Young Montrealers focused on other concerns — human rights abuses, cruelty to animals, widespread apathy, the effects of mass media upon society and the importance of education.

"The motto of the environmentally conscious consumer should be 'Reduce, re-use, recycle,' and things should be done in that order," said Rose Yen, an 18-year-old student at Vanier CEGEP.

She and other teens told how they tried to avoid taking plastic bags offered by stores and used up their lunch bags and scrap paper before putting them in recycling bins. Lachine High student Joanne Miller told how her hatred of litter resulted in her helping to clean a neighborhood park.

A couple of the Young Montrealers suggested, in gentle terms, that their forefathers might have done more to preserve their natural heritage.

"Our parents might have started up and realized this (environmental mess) might have happened but the generation before them said, 'We are going to die before anything happens,'" said Sebastien Chalifour, a Secondary 3 student at Polyvalente Ozias-Leduc.

"The reason why I feel the environment is something we should be paying more attention to is that in the past we have just been shoving the dirt under the carpet. We have not been dealing with any of the problems," said Simmi Chawla.

Chawla, editor of the Centennial Regional Secondary School yearbook, showed other panelists some examples of publications that use either unbleached or recycled paper.

Only 18 months ago, Debbie Horovitch believed that she didn't have to worry about the environment because "it was 200 years down the road when things would be changed slightly." Spurred by her mother, the Richelieu Valley Regional High School student started reading about environmental issues and learned "There are really big changes that are expected to happen if we don't do something soon about the environment."

Horovitch, now "full force" into the cause, keeps after her parents to conserve energy "so we don't have to produce more hydroelectric dams," separates paper from household garbage and encourages friends to recycle.

"I don't think I'm fanatical... because I still buy things that I know pollute the environment at one time or another and I drive my parents' car. If I really didn't want to pollute the environment, I'd stop driving," Horovitch said.

Tamara Ruby's concern for the environment has caused her to campaign for positive action at Trafalgar School for Girls. She and a couple of friends run Students Against Pollution Problems which deals with environmental issues and the plight of animals whose existence is threatened by pollution, the beluga whales being an example.

"Most people know that the environment is in trouble but they don't really know what to do," said Ruby, who is a member of her school's recycling group. She was also involved in a student bake sale this year to raise money so the school could "adopt" three humpback whales.

How best to tackle the gigantic problems posed by pollution was considered by a couple of the Young Montrealers.

Hovercraft were touted by Dustin Sean Isaacs as a solution to myriad problems facing South Shore commuters. They would be a godsend to the commuters who spend hours stuck on access bridges, generating clouds of exhaust, he said. Aside from cutting down on pollution, hovercraft "would reduce a heck of a lot of stress for commuters," said Isaacs, who brought in a model of a hovercraft that he and a classmate at Loyola High School had made.

Philippe Westreich, a Secondary 4 student at F.A.C.E. urged that more research be done on viable and affordable alternatives to the combustion engine. Motor vehicles make the biggest contribution to pollution, he said.

"If there were a way to concert all the jobs related to cars into jobs related to cleaning up the environment or providing different (energy sources) like solar energy, we would be fine," said Westreich.

The concern closest to Donna Shestowsky's heart is cruelty to animals. The Villa Maria High School student has researched the matter and written articles for her school newspaper and an interschool paper put out by Dawson CEGEP.

Treating animals properly "is not something that is just morally right, it is also something that is incorporated into the law. Not many people take that responsibility seriously," said Shestowsky, whose family has tended to a host of stray animals including a chicken — "probably an Easter pet" — that was found in her backyard in residential Brossard.

Chambly County Secondary School student Gavin Whitely argued that the effects of mass media on society are something that should be taken more seriously. The media's impact on young people was especially brought home at a recent conference he attended at school, the 16-year-old said.

The mass media "depict a world where sex, alcohol and violence are all over the place," said Whitely. As a result of the conference, pairs of Secondary 5 students are making the rounds of Secondary 2 humanities classes urging kids to postpone sexual involvement.

"The general concept is that Grade 8 students are more likely to listen to older students than to their teachers," he said.

Human rights abuses have to be a priority item on everyone's agenda for global improvements, said Sunil Gandhi, a Secondary 4 student at Chomedey Polyvalente.

"After you settle human rights then you can go after the environment," said Gandhi. "Look at apartheid in South Africa. (South Africans) have more important things on their mind than the environment."

Apathy is the enemy that has to be battled, Stephen Wark countered. Causes come and go, said Wark, using the famine in Ethiopia as an example of a "fad cause" that generated enormous concern and then fizzled, with people saying, "I did my part last year and I'm sick and tired of hearing about starving Africans.

"Once people are satisfied with what they have, they stop in their struggle, regardless of what other people might need," said Wark, a Richelieu Valley Regional High School student.

Education should be the main concern of teenagers, said Chantal Lelièvre. Not only does education enrich the student, it provides society with people who have the necessary knowledge and skills to advance it.

"In our contemporary society, education is the basis of everything," said Lelièvre, a Secondary 4 student at MacDonald Cartier Secondary who plans to study health science at CEGEP. "Right now, I'm devoting a lot of time, effort and perseverance to my studies because I know it will be rewarded in the future."

Trong-Qui Dao, a 15-year-old who attends John F. Kennedy High School, echoed Lelièvre's remarks.

"Before you can change the world, you have to change yourself," said Dao. "And education will help you accomplish your goals."

# Just How Committed Are We?

◆ ◆ ◆

**BY**

**RUPERT J.**

**TAYLOR**

## What a Waste

We, in the industrialized world, have never paid the true cost of our resource exploitation. One of the costs we've ignored is that of cleaning up the environmental messes our industries produce. Even now, many industries approach the problem of hazardous wastes by "sweeping them under the carpet." They do this by sending millions of tonnes of untreated toxic goo to the Third World.

Altogether, 81 countries now ban the importation of wastes; in Nigeria, the penalty for being caught doing so is death. However, that still leaves 90 or so countries that aren't too fussy about what comes ashore in unlabelled barrels.

It's estimated that Western businesses dumped 24 million tonnes of hazardous waste in West Africa alone in 1988. East Germany is thought to have earned between 10 and 20% of its hard currency from importing toxic waste. This was in the days before the communist government collapsed, and it's reasonable to assume most of that waste was just dumped untreated. It's said that Poland and Hungary also have active waste importing businesses. A waste importing scandal in Romania in 1989 saw some government officials jailed for up to 18 years.

Guinea-Bissau in West Africa was offered $600 million over five years to store 15 million tonnes of pharmaceutical and tanning waste. The $600 million is equal to four times the country's Gross Domestic Product. The deal was turned down after strong local protests.

And it's not just wastes that have been dumped. The United States exports 270 million kilos of pesticides each year, a quarter of which are either banned or severely restricted at home. A not unrelated statistic is, that of the roughly one million pesticide poisonings a year around the globe, the vast majority occur in the Third World. Between 5000 and 20 000 of these poisonings are fatal.

Estimated amount of tropical rainforest left untouched: 7.68 million km²

Number of years tropical rainforest will last at current rate of destruction: 30.5

Weight of carbon dioxide produced per person annually by industry: 3.3 tonnes

Weight of carbon dioxide exhaled by each human per year: 0.75 tonnes

Number of degrees Celsius the world's temperature has risen since the last Ice Age 18 000 years ago: 5

Concentration of PCBs called dangerous to public health by the federal government: 50 parts per million

Concentration of PCBs found in one shrew southeast of Montreal in 1989: 11 522 parts per million

Percentage increase in water usage in Canada between 1972 and 1981: 54

Percentage increase in Canada's population between 1972 and 1981: 5

Amount spent by Canadians on bottled water in 1986: $80 million; in 1989: $150 million

Percentage increase in solid waste disposed of by the city of Toronto between 1983 and 1987: 77

Estimated number of waste dumps in Canada: 8784

Number thought to present a health hazard: 526

Amount West African country of Benin charged per tonne for receiving industrial waste: $3

Cost per tonne of incinerating waste in North America: up to $2000

Number of synthetic chemicals currently in use: 70 000

Number of new synthetic chemicals added each year: 1000

Percentage of Canada's urban sewage that is untreated: more than 30

Percentage of Canadians in a Decima poll who thought pollution had affected their family's health very much or a fair amount in 1982: 53; in 1989: 81

## A Ten-Point Plan

Norway's prime minister, Gro Brundtland, was given a big assignment in 1983. She was asked by the United Nations to lead an independent World Commission on Environment and Development.

In 1987, Mrs. Brundtland presented her report, entitled, "Our Common Future." The Brundtland Report, as it has come to be called, highlighted the need for economic development to be undertaken in the context of sustainability.

A direct result, in Canada, was the setting up, by Prime Minister Brian Mulroney, of the National Round Table on the Environment and the Economy. This is a group of senior people from government, business, environmental organizations, and academic institutions. In its Annual Report, the Round Table published its objectives for sustainable development.

1. We must preserve the capacity of the biosphere to evolve by managing our social and economic activities for the benefit of present and future generations.

2. Everyone shares responsibility for a sustainable society.

3. We must try to anticipate and prevent future problems by avoiding the negative environmental, economic, social, and cultural impacts of policy, programs, decisions, and development activities.

4. We must maintain and enhance essential ecological processes, biological diversity, and life support systems.

5. We must reduce the energy and resource content of growth, harvest renewable resources on a sustainable basis, and make wise and efficient use of our non-renewable resources.

6. We must first endeavour to reduce the production of waste, then re-use, recycle and recover waste by-products.

7. We must try to rehabilitate and reclaim damaged environments.

8. We must support education and research and development of technologies, and goods and services essential to maintaining environmental quality, social and cultural values, and economic growth.

9. We must think globally when we act locally.

10. Canada should support methods that are consistent with the preceding objectives when helping developing countries.

## Just How Committed Are We?

A public opinion poll in the spring of 1990 suggests that Canadians have mixed feelings about protecting the environment. Yes, we want a clean world, but, no, we don't want to give up any goodies to get it. The Angus Reid poll found that:

- About 60% of Canadians oppose banning private cars from cities during certain hours, or applying tax on parking.
- Nearly 75% oppose adding a special fuel tax on all cars in cities.
- More than 50% oppose charging for garbage pickup based on how much individuals throw out.
- More than 50% oppose a tax on packaging to reduce the amount used.
- More than 50% oppose increases in downtown residential density as a way to limit urban sprawl.

# Memo to
# the 21st Century

♦ ♦ ♦

BY

PHILIP

APPLEMAN

It was like this once: sprinklers mixed
our marigolds with someone else's phlox,
and the sidewalks under maple trees
were lacy with August shade,
and whistles called at eight and fathers walked
to work, and when they blew again,
men in tired blue shirts followed
their shadows home to grass.
That is how it was in Indiana.

Towns fingered out to country once,
where brown-eyed daisies waved a fringe on
      orchards
and cattle munched at clover, and
fishermen sat in rowboats and were silent,
and on gravel roads, boys and girls
stopped their cars and felt the moon and touched,
and the quiet moments ringed and focused
lakes        moons        flowers.
That is how it was
in Indiana.

But we are moving out now,
scraping the world smooth where apples blossomed,
paving it over for cars. In the spring
before the clover goes purple,
we mean to scrape the hayfield, and
next year the hickory woods:
we are pushing on, our giant diesels snarling,
and I think of you, the billions of you, wrapped
in your twenty-first century concrete,
and I want to call to you, to let you know
that if you dig down,
down past wires and pipes
and sewers and subways, you will find
a crumbly stuff called earth. Listen:
in Indiana once, things grew in it.

# Requiem for a River

♦ ♦ ♦

**BY KIM WILLIAMS**

"So we diverted the river," he said,
showing blueprints
and maps
and geological surveys.
"It'll go in this canal now."

The Rio Blanco River starts in a glacier
up the white-capped Andes.
It has run through a green valley
for three million years,
maybe more.

Now in this year
when the Rio Blanco copper mine
at 12,000 feet altitude
gets underway,
the river has to go.

Pick it up,
Move it over —
Anything is possible.
Don't stand in the way
of progress,
And a 90-million-dollar mine.
"We concreted the dam," Bert said.

Thanks.

# Digging In

♦ ♦ ♦

### BY

### ELIZABETH

### BREWSTER

Eight thousand years ago
according to the archaeologist on the radio
there were people living
on the Manitoba plains

long before the Pharaohs
and the Hanging Gardens of Babylon
long before Troy and Homer

long before Socrates or Sophocles
long before the Roman legions
before Boadicea and Beowulf

ages before Burbage stepped out
on the stage of the Globe

ages before Columbus, Cook, Vancouver
were discovered by the natives
of the so-called New World

their campfires were burning
they trapped animals
skinned them for leather

talked, sang songs maybe
hushed the children
watched the pictures
in the fire

left garbage behind
as we do

You know a people
the archaeologist says
by their garbage

though much of it of course
moulders away
returns to earth.

What, I wonder,
might be left
eight thousand years from now
of the kitchen where I'm sitting
eating an apple and
listening to the radio?

Not books, newspapers, apple cores
Not my own bones
Not the works of my radio
or of my microwave oven

but a few scraps of metal
maybe plastic
a knife, a fork

a dishwasher-proof
butter dish, milk jug

evidence, so someone may say,
of primitive life
responding to basic needs.

# National Totems

## Mountain Gorilla and Giant Panda

◆ ◆ ◆

**BY**

**DAVID**

**DAY**

**S**ince prehistoric times, people have seen certain characteristics in animals which they admire, and they have adopted these as emblematic animals for their tribe, race or nation. This is no less true today than it was in ancient times. Most nations have at least one animal that serves as a kind of national totem. Sometimes they are exotic or even mythical animals: lion for Britain, unicorn for France. However, most often they are animals native to those countries: bear for Russia, eagle for the United States, elephant for India, beaver for Canada, kangaroo for Australia, kiwi for New Zealand.

Like most tribal people who adopt a totem animal, most nations take an active concern in survival of these special animals and, in modern times, have often found it necessary to take measures to guard against the possibility of those animals becoming extinct.

In the twentieth century, there have been a number of creatures that have been saved from over-exploitation by becoming national totems. The eagle in America and the beaver in Canada were both species that were becoming endangered because of overhunting until appeals to national pride successfully mobilized the governments of these nations and the totemic animals were protected and revived.

Realizing how successful such tactics can be, conservationists have often lobbied for the adoption of some unique national or state animal in an attempt to save a species from extinction. This is certainly true of most American states. A few years ago conservationists convinced Connecticut to adopt the Sperm Whale as its state animal. Consequently, Connecticut has taken an active interest in the Save the Whale movement world-wide. The spectacularly beautiful and nearly extinct

Monkey-eating Eagle had a new lease of life when it was renamed the Philippine Eagle and became the national bird. Laws were immediately passed for its protection and it was granted a territorial refuge and a captive breeding programme was funded by the federal government.

Similarly, it was largely because of the celebrity status achieved by the Mountain Gorillas through the work of the dedicated conservationist Dian Fossey that the African nation of Rwanda acquired these remarkable animals as national totems. Although Mountain Gorillas are among the world's most endangered species, the three hundred or so remaining animals may very well survive because of their special status in this small, poor African nation. Rwanda will ensure their continued existence for a long time to come as the animals will continue to be a major source of income through tourism.

One of the best known and certainly most popular of all the more recently acquired national totems must be the Giant Panda (*Ailuropoda melanoleuca*) of China. Rare, exotic, cuddly, playful, gentle and strikingly handsome, the Giant Panda — ever since the world beyond China learned of its existence — has been one of the most popular animals on the planet. It was not until quite recently, however, that China itself learned of the Panda's great powers as an international diplomat and ambassador of goodwill for the Chinese nation. Today it is a national treasure. Although it is a very rare animal — probably no more than 1000 exist — the Chinese have recently taken the species' survival very much to heart, banning all hunting absolutely, and only allowing capture with government approval on a national level.

The Panda has always been a rare and mysterious beast. There are a few ancient Chinese written accounts of the trade in skins of these animals — usually called "Bei-shung" or "white bear" — in ancient Chinese writings. Even in ancient times the Panda was extremely rare and made its home largely in the remote bamboo forests of mountainous Szechwan province, so the Chinese themselves were largely unaware of this secretive animal's existence.

The story of the coming of the first Pandas to the West is a dramatic and surprisingly recent one. Western science was first to learn of the existence of this mysterious animal through the explorations of a remarkable French priest, Father Armand

David. Father David, or Père David as he is usually known, was a Jesuit priest who became the greatest authority of his time on Chinese flora and fauna. In 1869 Père David first heard of this mysterious animal and was shown a skin by a hunter in the remote mountainous and forested regions of the southern province of Szechwan. In the following weeks, Père David was able to acquire two skins of his own by paying local hunters to track the animals down. He made notes on how the animal was totally unlike any other species of bear in many structural aspects, and also as it lived almost entirely on bamboo. Soon after, when Père David's Chinese bear skins arrived in Paris and were called various names from Harlequin Bear to Bamboo Bear, it was immediately established that they belonged to a unique species.

And unique the Giant Panda certainly is; even today there is considerable debate about how to classify the animal. Some classify it as an early form of bear, others as a specialized member of the racoon family, others still believe it should be classified in a family grouping uniquely its own. Today, everyone is familiar with the general appearance of the Giant Panda and generally think of it as a large, living cuddly toy.

A large adult Giant Panda however, grows up to weigh as much as 135 kg (300 lb.) and measures up to 1.8 m (6 ft.) in length. When born the animal is entirely white and weighs less than 450 g (1 lb.), but grows to about 30 kg (70 lb.) within a year. It is quite a solitary animal, living alone in areas of bamboo and coniferous forest and foraging for vast quantities of bamboo shoots every day. The Giant Panda makes itself beds of bamboo in lairs under the shelter of hollow trees or overhanging rocks and lives at altitudes of between 2500 and 4000 m (8000 and 13,000 ft.) in a generally cold and humid climate. Unlike other bears, in the extreme cold of winter, the Panda does not hibernate but simply moves further down the mountainside out of the worst of the weather. The life span of the Giant Panda is believed to be a little over fifteen years.

After Père David's initial discovery of the Giant Panda, six more skins reached the West through traders over the next several decades but very little further information came out of China about this mysterious animal. In fact, it was nearly another fifty years before a westerner actually saw a live Giant Panda.

This happened in the year 1916, when the German zoologist Hugo Weigold went on an expedition into West China and Tibet and, through local hunters, actually acquired a live infant Panda. Sadly the infant did not survive long and died shortly after Weigold bought it. Still, this would normally have been a remarkable encounter, at least in scientific circles, but as this expedition had been launched by the Germans in the midst of World War I, Weigold's news did not reach Britain or America. Even a decade or more afterwards, other adventurers who set out in search of the Giant Panda were unaware of Weigold's first encounter with a living Panda.

Up to now, all the Giant Pandas had been killed or captured by Chinese hunters or the Lolo tribesmen who inhabited the region and no westerner could claim to have personally tracked down and shot a Giant Panda. As might be expected, this sort of challenge appealed less to the zoologists and more to the big-game hunting fraternity.

In 1928, two hunters achieved their greatest ambition. At enormous cost, the Americans Theodore and Kermit Roosevelt set out on a highly publicized expedition to track down the Giant Panda. It seems somewhat ironic that these two intrepid hunters were the sons of the American President Theodore (or

Teddy) Roosevelt. After all, the famous "Teddy Bear" was named after Roosevelt by a toy manufacturer when the press reported how the President proved too soft-hearted to shoot a little brown bear cub while on a hunting trip, and insisted on it being released. Kermit and Theodore Jr. had no such pangs of conscience when tracking down the Giant Panda — the future challenger to the Teddy Bear as the child's favourite cuddly toy. Determined to become the first great white hunters to bag a Giant Panda, their hearts did not soften when the opportunity came.

Kermit Roosevelt wrote of that first fatal encounter with the Panda in his book *Trailing the Giant Panda:*

"On the morning of the 13th of April we came upon Giant Panda tracks in the snow near Yehli, south of Tachienlu in the Hsifan mountains. The animal had evidently passed a goodish while before the snow ceased falling, but some sign that one of the Lolos found proved to be recent enough to thoroughly arouse all four natives...

"We had been following the trail for two and a half hours when we came to a more open jungle. Unexpectedly close I heard a clicking chirp. One of the Lolo hunters darted forward. He had not gone forty yards before he turned back to eagerly motion to us to hurry. As I gained his side he pointed to a giant spruce thirty yards away. The bole was hollowed, and from it emerged the head and forequarters of a Beishung. He looked sleepily from side to side as he sauntered forth and walked slowly away into the bamboo. As soon as Ted came up we fired simultaneously at the outline of the disappearing Panda. Both shots took effect. He was a splendid old male, the first that the Lolos had any record of as being killed in this Yehli region. Our great good fortune could only with much effort be credited. After so long holding aloof, the Hunting Gods had turned about and brewed the unusual chain of circumstances that alone could enable us to shoot a Giant Panda, trailing him without dogs and with the crowning bit of luck that permitted us to fire jointly."

It is hard for most people today to feel much joy in this account of the killing of this gentle, harmless animal, but it was a major event at the time, and most of the main natural history institutes in the world wanted their own Giant Panda skins. For the next decade, despite their acknowledged rarity and the very real possibility of their near-extinct status, there was an all-out attempt to track down and kill as many Giant Pandas as possible. A number of expeditions were sent out to hunt them down and discover as much as could be found out about them. One expedition leader went so far as to test out the Panda as a source of food (the local people did not eat the animals) and was the first — and hopefully the last — westerner to eat Giant Panda steaks. Fortunately for the animal the steaks proved very tough, and it was thought that even as Panda hamburger, it would not be very palatable.

By 1936, a total of nearly thirty Giant Pandas had been slaughtered for western collections. By that time, it occured to some westerners that as rare and exciting as the acquisition of Giant Pandas for the purpose of stuffing and displaying might be, the acquisition of a live specimen as a zoo animal would have enormous public appeal.

And so, once again, another great Giant Panda race was on. Who would be the first to bring in a live Giant Panda?

Considering the difficulty of even finding live animals to shoot, many thought the elusive animal would prove next to impossible to trap alive. However, in 1936, there were two front-runners in this race;

an experienced animal collector with the colourful and unlikely name of Floyd Tangier Smith and a New York fashion designer named Ruth Harkness. Floyd Tangier Smith had spent over a decade in the region and had helped acquire a number of Panda skins for collectors. Ruth Harkness had never been to the Orient before and knew next to nothing about Giant Pandas, except that it had been her late husband's dream to capture one.

Tangier Smith and most others with knowledge of the bandit-ridden region thought it preposterous that a woman should even attempt to travel in Panda territory, let alone embark on such an impossible mission as actually to capture one. But Ruth Harkness penetrated the extraordinary wilderness with terrific tenacity, and captured a baby Giant Panda with the help of the Chinese-American hunter Quentin Young.

In her book *The Lady and the Panda,* Ruth Harkness writes with some humour about the almost unbelievably difficult time she had in making it into Panda country. On the critical day in November when they neared their quarry at last, Ruth Harkness describes her far from dignified pursuit. With Quentin Young and a local hunter ahead of her, she was making her way through the undergrowth:

"...mostly on hands and knees, only Yang remained behind to give me an occasional lift by the seat of my pants. Without warning, a shout went up from the jungle ahead of us. I heard Lao yell, the report of his blunderbuss musket, and then Quentin's voice raised in rapid and imperious Chinese. Falling, stumbling, or being dragged by Yang, we crashed through the bamboo."

A full-grown Giant Panda had crossed their trail and one of the hunters, against instruction, had fired his gun. The frightened animal fled, but Quentin Young and Ruth Harkness did not follow the hunters.

"We listened for a moment, and went on a few yards farther where the bamboo thinned slightly, giving way to a few big trees. Quentin stopped so short that I almost fell over him. He listened intently for a split second, and then went ploughing on so rapidly I couldn't keep up with him. Dimly through the waving wet branches I saw him near a huge rotting tree. I too stopped, frozen in my tracks. From the old dead tree came a baby's whimper. I must have been momentarily paralyzed, for I didn't move until Quentin came toward me and held out his arms. There in the palms of his two hands was a squirming baby Beishung."

It was a ten-day-old Panda weighing less than three pounds. Its eyes were still closed and Ruth Harkness bottle-fed the animal and raised it like a kitten. She named it Su-Lin which means "something very cute." After numerous other adventures attempting to get her little passenger safely out of China, Ruth Harkness at last succeeded in bringing the first live Giant Panda to the West.

So the first Giant Panda to reach the West alive found its home in the Brookfield Zoo in Chicago in 1937, and the following year was joined by a second Giant Panda called Mei-Mei, which again was captured by Ruth Harkness.

Meanwhile, the intrepid Floyd Tangier Smith proved he was not entirely out of the Giant Panda competitions. In 1938, Tangier Smith arrived in England on a ship packed with no less than five live Pandas, tentatively called Grandma, Happy, Dopey, Grumpy and Baby. The last three were purchased by the London Zoo and renamed Sung, Tang and Ming.

Only six more live Giant Pandas were to be exported to the West before the Chinese government in 1941 placed an absolute ban on their export. With only one exception, there were no more live Pandas allowed outside China for sixteen years. In some respects this was something of a blessing, for zoos knew too little of these animals to care for them properly. Of the fourteen animals reaching the West only four survived more than four years, and only one more than ten years, and so for a time there were no Giant Pandas at all in zoos.

However, between 1957 and 1959, a total of three Giant Pandas were presented by the Chinese government. Two of these (called Ping-Ping and An-An) went to the Moscow Zoo, and one (called Chi-Chi) to the London Zoo. Fortunately, understanding of Panda habits and biology had increased to some degree and these zoos proved safer places for the animals than before. Although Ping-Ping died in 1961, Chi-Chi and An-An went on to break all records and were both nearly fifteen years old when they died. For all of that time these animals were the only live Pandas in existence outside China.

In 1972, all that was to change, for the Chinese government opened its doors to the West. As a historic gesture, when Richard Nixon became the first American President to visit China, the Chinese government made a gift of a Giant Panda to the Washington Zoo. The West once again had a Giant Panda.

Since then, about twenty Giant Pandas have been officially presented to national governments as tokens of friendship, and an international effort launched by such organizations as the World Wildlife Fund has been made to protect the species in the wild. The Chinese government has matched the enthusiasm of these organizations and set up over a hundred reserves and a number of study centres. The animals are notoriously difficult to breed in captivity, although institutions in China have had noted successes, and artificial insemination programmes look likely to be established in the future.

Today more is known about Giant Pandas than ever before, but essentially they remain rare, mysterious and fascinating creatures. Now that the Chinese government and the international conservation community have taken an active and protective interest in the animal, its survival seems likely. It appears as if the thousand or so Giant Pandas left may very well have established a secure place on this planet — and they will have succeeded in doing so largely by establishing a secure place in the hearts of members of the human race.

# Drawing the Line in the Vanishing Jungle

♦ ♦ ♦

BY

DAVID M. SCHWARTZ

**A**t dawn, the owl-like hoot of a rufous mot-mot penetrates the fog of Ecuador's coastal rain forest. All around me, drops from last night's downpour cascade from the leafy canopy more than a hundred feet [30 m] overhead. Shrouded in the eerie mist, I am completely disoriented, but fortunately my Awá Indian companions know the way.

We slog through calf-deep mud, pulling hard to extract our boots at every step. The going is tough but worth the effort, I remind myself, for soon we will arrive at a sight unique in all the jungle—the *manga*. To the casual observer, the manga is a simple, broad path snaking through the underbrush. To the Awá, it may be the fine line between survival and ruin.

The Awá Indians that live along the border of Ecuador and Colombia are among the many native populations sprinkled across the map of South America. About 2200 Awá make their home in Ecuador, and another 5000 in Colombia. For centuries, these people have led lives of quiet isolation, virtually unknown to the outside world until about a decade ago.

The Awá are part of a complex ecological web of dense flora and teeming fauna in what may be the most biologically diverse quarter-million acres in the world. By taking only what they need, the Indians have preserved the 300 species of plants and animals they harvest for shelter, food and fiber. They seem the model of a people at one with their environment. But that environment is critically endangered — and so, as a result, are the Awá.

My trek to the heart of Awá territory has taken me to a remote village in northwestern Ecuador, a journey that required

a full day's paddling in a dugout canoe. Welcomed as a guest of the Awá, I am getting a firsthand look at a people struggling against overwhelming odds to save their place in the rain forest.

Forces of change bear down hard on the region, and the Awá are caught in the squeeze. To the east, cattle ranchers have carved rangeland out of vast tracts of forest. In the west, loggers are stripping the land. To the north, in Colombia, plantations have transformed the jungle into immense monocultures of palm trees grown for oil. From all sides, *colonos* (colonists) have invaded Awá lands, clearing trees, overhunting game, fishing with dynamite and settling wherever they like.

"At the current rate of deforestation," says Carlos Villareal, a government economist who works with the Awá, "the Pacific coastal rain forest of Ecuador will be completely gone by the year 2000, and the acute social and economic problems that already exist will blow up."

In 1985, the Awá began an extraordinary battle against the forces working to destroy their home and way of life. With the help of a former U.S. Peace Corps volunteer and a national coalition of Indians, the tribe established its first government, the Awá Federation, and built shelters for community centers. Within just a few years, these hitherto uneducated tribespeople had built schools and convinced the Ecuadorean government to train members of their community as teachers and health-care educators.

At times the Awá have had to reinforce their claims to the land with steel and gunpowder. More than once, they have taken up machetes and *escopetas* to scare away intruders. But no weapon in the Awá arsenal has proved as powerful as the novel land-management technique they call the manga.

The manga is nothing more than a 150-mile [241-km] long serpentine swath encircling Awá territory, carved out of the very rain forest the Indians wish to preserve. It is also nothing less than a demonstration of the power of positive action, and a model for other indigenous peoples trying to discourage deforestation on their own turf. In 1988, largely because of the manga, Ecuador's government designated Awá lands an "Ethnic Forest Reserve," South America's first such sanctuary. The Awá Reserve represents a stunning victory not only for the Indians, but for all the species that share their threatened home.

As my Awá guides and I make our way through the forest toward the edge of the Reserve, the mist lifts. Hazy sunlight dances off the Río Bagatá. After fording the river, we reenter the jungle, darkened by the filter of leaves, lianas and tree trunks. We trudge uphill for 15 minutes. Then the light intensifies once again as we emerge in an open corridor: the manga. At first sight it is unremarkable — a clearing dotted with cultivated trees. But as my companions proudly explain, stripping this land was the best thing they ever did to preserve the forest.

Whisking their machetes, the Awá go to work clearing out the tangle of weeds that have invaded since their last visit. In just a few months, second-growth trees such as balsa have sent up shoots 8 inches [20 cm] thick and 30 feet [9 m] high. It takes a trained eye to distinguish unwanted plants from the cash crops: *borojó*, whose mineral-rich fruits can fetch more than a dollar apiece in Colombia; *gualte*, a sturdy wood used for home construction; *bacao*, a wild chocolate; *chonta duro*, a spiny-trunked palm that produces tasty pulp; and familiar crops—breadfruit, soursop, cacao, coffee—which can be sold for a profit.

It will be years before any of the plants can be harvested, I'm told. Sensing my disappointment, a young Awá boy wielding a machete as long as his arm chops down a small palm and deftly removes the heart. I accept it as a delicious snack.

To a people whose jungle is their castle, the manga is the "moat" that keeps intruders at bay, though its surface is solid ground, essentially unguarded and easily crossed. "The manga announces our land and tells everyone that the Awá live here," says Julian Cantincuz, president of the Awá Federation. In the borderless expanse of jungle, he says, colonos who know exactly where the Awá lands begin will be less likely to invade —especially when the boundary is trumpeted by a clearing that, like a line drawn in the sand, proclaims, "Cross this and you're in for a fight."

But more than a tool for self-defense, the manga is also a rallying point for community organization. "The manga assures that we will work together," says Cantincuz. "So long as the Awá are united, no one will take advantage of us."

Standing less than five feet [1.5 m] tall, Cantincuz, like many Awá tribesmen, has a physical strength that belies his stature. Some of that strength is no doubt the result of the many hours he spends with his fellow tribesmen swinging a machete and planting crops in the manga.

Indeed, the sheer physical labor the manga represents adds immeasureably to its value: A project so large and tangible commands respect from Ecuador's government, which is often skeptical of Indian land claims. "When we talk to government officials, the manga backs us up," says Cantincuz. "They know this is Awá land. We have the manga to prove it."

In Ecuador, as in most of South America, indigenous peoples cannot control the land they have occupied for millennia unless they obtain legal title. The government, citing the need for economic development, prefers to award title only to those who promise to "improve" the forest by putting it to "productive" use. Usually that means cutting it down. Time and again, poor and politically powerless Indians have fallen victim to non-indigenous populations who get the nod from the government to exploit the land for their own short-term goals.

The Awá took their first steps toward self-determination in the mid-1980s, when they learned that an agricultural cooperative had designs on a 6000-acre [2428-ha] plot in Awá territory. Meanwhile, a number of timber companies were planning to purchase wood rights nearby. Some had already intimidated Awá tribesmen into putting their thumbprints on contracts selling all land for less than one cent an acre.

Tribal leaders called an emergency meeting and invited a man named Jim Levy to attend. A former Peace Corps volunteer who had helped the Awá organize to defend their territory, Levy put forth an idea: Why not cut a giant trail around all the tribe's land in one continuous swath? Not just a narrow footpath easily ignored and quickly overcome by jungle growth, but a 30- to 45-foot-wide [9- to 14-m] manga (line of demarcation) enclosing the tribe's domain.

The Awá saw that the manga would help identify their land. Levy pointed out that it could do much more. With planting and cultivation, fruit and nut trees might grow in the manga and some day bring needed income. With a little extra vigilance, tribesmen posted to keep the manga clear of jungle overgrowth could serve as sentries, watching out for intruders. Colonos who crossed onto Awá lands could be ejected at once.

Most important, cutting the manga meant, in the eyes of the government, that the Awá were putting their land to "productive" use. The manga was the tribe's best hope for establishing a claim to ownership, possibly even title.

"The most striking thing the Awá have done with the manga is demonstrate to themselves and the country that you don't have to take an environmentally destructive and ecologically shortsighted approach to prove that you are using land," says Ted Macdonald, project director for Cultural Survival, a Massachusetts-based group that helps indigenous people like the Awá gain economic self-sufficiency.

In 1986, evidently hearing the message, Ecuador's government responded by mapping out the manga and awarding long-denied citizenship papers to the Awá. Two years later, the government created the Awá Reserve. While less secure than title, Reserve status prohibits logging and keeps intruders out, thus enabling the Awá to manage their own natural resources.

The system has proven so effective that others want to try it as well. Across the border, the Awá of Colombia face most of the same problems as their Ecuadorean brethren. Having seen the manga work for their kin, the Colombians now plan to create one of their own.

At least two other tribes, the Huaorani of eastern Ecuador and the Embera of Colombia, have already started cutting mangas around their land. Meanwhile, the directors of the Rio Palanche Reserve, Colombia's largest wildlife sanctuary, are considering using the manga concepts as a land-management tool.

The creation of the Awá Reserve has heartened not only indigenous peoples, but biologists and conservationists worldwide. With 300 to 400 inches [762 to 1016 cm] of rainfall a year, the Reserve is one of the rainiest places on Earth. Because rainfall correlates closely with species number, it is also wondrously diverse. "Biologically, this is probably the richest area in Ecuador," says Calaway Dodson, senior curator of the Missouri Botanical Garden and Director of Ecuador's National Herbarium. "And Ecuador is biologically the richest country in the world," he continues. "It is definitely an area worth saving."

Dodson and other biologists who have studied the area credit it with uncounted thousands of plant species, many rare fish and amphibians, and more than 600 birds, along with five cats, four monkeys and the highly endangered spectacled bear. About 40 bird species and six percent of the plants in the Reserve are believed to be found nowhere else.

Conservationists are beginning to recognize that the key to saving the rain forest is to join forces with the people who live there. With that goal in mind, environmentalists from around the world met in Peru last year with representatives from 327 South American tribes and pledged to work together. Even so, optimism and international support are no assurance that indigenous people like the Awá will succeed at protecting their land. Too many hazards lurk on the murky edges of the political and economic landscape.

An island of protected habitat in a sea of environmental degradation, the Awá Reserve may ultimately be swept aside. Communal land title remains an elusive goal for the Awá, and without it the government could dissolve the Reserve with a stroke of the pen. Furthermore, the "gold fever" that has infected much of South America could easily spread inside the Reserve. Gold-mining companies already operate just outside its borders, and because the Reserve's protected status doesn't exclude mining, there's too little to stop them from moving in.

The most pressing danger to the Awá, however, comes from their 70 000 neighbours in the San Lorenzo area, the country's most impoverished corner. These non-indigenous people — nearly half of whom live by wood exploitation — are as bent on consuming the rain forest as the Indians are determined to

sustain it.

After leaving the manga, three of my Awá companions accompany me to a community house where we will spend the night. Along the way, a young man stoops to point out a log set between two rows of wooden pegs — a deadfall trap baited for *ratón puyazo* (spiny rat), an important meat source. "Each family has at least 50 traps spread out over a large area," the man explains. "Once we make a catch, we do not use that trap again for three months. This way there will be puyazo for our children."

He disappears down the trail while I linger at the trap. This, I realize, is the fundamental difference between the Awá and their neighbors: The Indians are concerned about leaving natural resources for their children. Outsiders concentrate only on what they can take today.

"The Reserve is one of the last stocks of intact natural resources in the region," says Carlos Villareal. "When the rest is gone, the people of the area are not going to sit back and starve to death quietly." Since 1983, Villareal has directed a small government agency called the Unidad Tecnica del Plan Awá (UTEPA), which acts as official advocate for the Awá. Since the creation of the Awá Reserve,

UTEPA has focused on helping the area's other non-indigenous populations find economic alternatives to plundering the rain forest and selling the spoils.

Projects funded by UTEPA so far include demonstration farms, where pigs are raised on sugar concentrates to show *campesinos* they can earn as much by raising swine on 2 [0.8 hectares] acres of sugarcane as by ranching cattle on 20 acres [8 hectares] of pasture. At one site, pig manure feeds fish in artificial ponds, and sludge from the ponds is used to fertilize sugarcane.

What began as an obscure Indian tribe's struggle to protect its homeland has evolved into a complex network of interrelated projects. And what appeared a few years ago as a dark future for the Awá and their neighbors is now brighter — still uncertain but streaked with hope.

After leaving the Awá, I stop in San Lorenzo, a raw-edged city of poverty and disease, before beginning my journey home. I depart at dawn on the *autoferro*, a converted bus mounted on a railway chassis that hairpins up the west slope of the Andes, affording a panorama of the Awá Reserve. Its great green vastness falls away to the horizon, so tranquil yet so tenuous in its coveted lushness.

I ponder the many interrelated pieces of this huge puzzle and wonder what lies ahead for the region. I recall something Carlos Villareal told me over lunch on the day I left for the Reserve. "Just as you can't talk about protecting birds and forget about the trees," he said, "you can't talk about protecting the rain forest and forget the people who live there." On a napkin he drew interlinking ovals to represent the interdependent elements of the ecosystem.

"And if you talk about protecting indigenous people," he continued, "you can't forget the non-indigenous people who live all around them." Now, with all the links in place, there is finally a chance to save the chain.

# A Poem for the Rainforest

◆ ◆ ◆

## BY JUDITH NICHOLLS

*Song of the Xingu Indian*

They have stolen my land;
the birds have flown,
my people gone.
My rainbow rises over sand,
my river falls on stone.

*Amazonian Timbers, Inc.*

This can go next —
here, let me draw the line.
That's roughly right,
give or take
a few square miles or so.
I'll list the ones we need.
No, burn the rest.
Only take the best,
we're not in this
for charity.
Replant? No —
*you're* new to this, I see!
There's plenty more
where that comes from,
no problem! Finish here —
and then move on.

*Dusk*

Butterfly, blinded
by smoke, drifts like torn paper
to the flames below.

*Shadows*

Spider,
last of her kind,
scuttles underground, safe;
prepares her nest for young ones. But
none come.

*The Coming of Night*

Sun sinks
behind the high canopy;
the iron men are silenced.

The moon rises,
the firefly wakes.
Death pauses for a night.

*Song of the Forest*

Our land has gone,
our people flown.
Sun scorches our earth,
our river weeps.

# The Fragile Land

♦ ♦ ♦

**BY**

**JANICE**

**HAMILTON**

**M**ost people think of the Arctic as one of the cleanest places on Earth with all that pure, white snow and clear blue sky. After all, it is thousands of kilometres away from the industries that create smog over cities such as Toronto.

Unfortunately, most people are wrong. Across the Arctic, empty or half-filled oil drums litter the countryside. Residents worry about the danger of oil spills from exploration wells or shipping accidents. Each spring, a phenomenon known as Arctic haze spreads a brown pall over the landscape. First noticed in the 1950s, it is made up of soot, sulphates and other industrial pollutants, and reduces visibility

from the normal 100 kilometres to 20 kilometres. Another serious pollution threat is unseen: industrial chemicals that have made their way into the Arctic food chain.

"People think of the Arctic as isolated, pristine, and unchanging," says Alan Saunders, communications director of the Ottawa-based Canadian Arctic Resources Committee. "They forget it is attached to the rest of the world. But nature has made the Arctic a natural catch-all basin for pollution. For the greater part of the year, weather systems across Siberia blow airborne pollutants northward, and the North Atlantic current drifts up past Greenland toward the Arctic Ocean. This means a lot of pollution ends up in the Arctic and doesn't leave."

The sources of the pollution that affects the Canadian Arctic are indeed far away. A study published in the respected British scientific journal *Nature* proves that much of the sulphur that causes Arctic haze every spring comes from coal-fired power plants and smelters in Europe and the Soviet Union. A previous study showed that lead contaminating the Arctic food chain comes from Eurasian industries. One pesticide, a chemical used on cotton plants, is thought to originate in

Southeast Asia. Scientists suspect other pesticides which have been banned in Canada and the United States for many years come to the Arctic from the Soviet Union.

Toxins such as PCBs and related dioxins and furans are released from industrial smokestacks. They travel on air currents until they fall on the land and water of the Arctic. Pesticides such as DDT get into the air through agricultural spraying or evaporation, then are also carried on the air currents. Other pollutants are transported in rivers that drain ten million square kilometres of northern Asia, Europe, and North America as far south as the 50th parallel.

But, certain characteristics of the Arctic make the situation worse. First, notes Saunders, pollutants that are covered by ice are difficult to detect and to clean up. The dry climate and freezing temperatures mean the system does not flush itself clean regularly, as happens in warmer regions. Pollutants are not broken down by the sun and other natural processes.

Finally, these pollutants accumulate in the fat and livers of animals at the top of the food chain — animals such as seals and whales that form the basis of the Inuit diet. A recent study showed Arctic beluga whales killed by native hunters have far higher levels of cadmium — a heavy metal and common industrial pollutant — than belugas in the St. Lawrence River. High levels of cadmium were found in the liver, kidneys, and muscle tissue. There were also high mercury levels in the whale muscle tissue. Such heavy metals are associated with a variety of health problems.

Scientists say the whales must be picking up these contaminants from their food. However, it's not known whether the pollution is widespread, whether it is limited to specific areas of the ocean, or whether heavy metals occur naturally in the Arctic environment.

In 1989, the results of a study carried out on Broughton Island, off the eastern shore of Baffin Island, shocked many Inuit. It showed that 63% of the children tested and 39% of the women of childbearing age had blood levels of PCBs that exceeded what the federal government considers to be "tolerable." (In this case, tolerable means the amount that can be eaten daily over a long period of time with no harmful effects.) High levels of PCBs also showed up in breast milk. The people show no signs of sickness that could be linked to these chemicals. Scientists have told them it's better to continue eating their traditional diet than to switch to less nutritious store-bought foods. Nevertheless, the study left them worried and confused.

Arctic pollution is an international problem, so international cooperation is needed to find solutions. This has begun to happen. In 1989, representatives of eight circumpolar nations — Canada, the United States, the Soviet Union, Sweden, Finland, Norway, Iceland, and Denmark — met in Finland to establish priorities and strategies for clean-up action. Meanwhile, scientists with interests in this field have set up an International Arctic Science Committee to coordinate and standardize research. Scientists admit they know very little about the effects of pollution on the Arctic environment.

Native northerners have also been meeting with each other to discuss this issue that so directly affects them. The Inuit Circumpolar Conference, an organization that represents more than 100 000 Inuit in Canada, Greenland, and Alaska, is doing its own environmental studies and planning. It has called for a global agreement to reduce the production of toxic chemicals that threaten the North.

There is a growing recognition of the Arctic pollution problem by countries with land masses north of the Arctic Circle. There remains a problem of how to deal with polluters which are not Arctic states, Saunders points out.

Another problem is that, even though the technology to install pollution controls and build cleaner industrial smelters and factories now exists, the money for such projects cannot always be found. Saunders visited the city of Norilsk in the Soviet Union. He called it "an environmental nightmare 300 kilometres above the Arctic Circle." Its nickel, copper, and other smelters use old, inefficient technology that creates a lot of pollution. But, with the Soviet Union's current economic crisis, the country can neither afford to shut down nor to upgrade these industries.

Saunders is optimistic about the pace at which governments are moving to tackle this problem. However, he adds, there must also be activity at the grassroots level in countries such as the Soviet Union if real progress is to be made. That means environmental activists from the West have to make contact with groups there. They have to help get the message across that something can and must be done.

# Incredible Inedible Pie

♦ ♦ ♦

BY

ROBERT

PRIEST


Take a poison boysenberry
and an oil slick from the sea
and mix it up with mercury
sauteed in p.c.b.
add in two cups of toxic waste
and two tears from each eye
blend in some tomato paste
INCREDIBLE, INEDIBLE PIE!

Take one valley and fill it up
with dusty uranium tailings
take radioactive albatross
and stuff scraped off of railings
mix it in with some acid rain
and some smoke from the summer sky
blend in two pieces of plutonium
INCREDIBLE, INEDIBLE PIE
You can pass my piece right by
INCREDIBLE INEDIBLE PIE!

# Beggarman

♦ ♦ ♦

**BY**

**SUSAN**

**SHWARTZ**

"**A**nd see the wounded world healed in my dreams..."

One more line, and he'd have the poem finished. Earth bobbed in the viewport—or maybe he bobbed in zero G; it was hard to tell—fragile and bright like the enormous soap bubbles you could blow in zero G if you weren't worrying about antisocial behavior.

Oh, this was going to be one good poem—maybe the best he'd ever written! He could just hear it...

"The wounded world," he says. "The wooouunnded wor-ulld! Jommy, you're such a throwback!"

Jolted from his thoughts, Jommy started, bouncing at least a meter in the Rim's zero G as Andrew and Mira snatched at his poems, gracefully, careful to conserve motion. Just his luck. The most popular kids on the Habitat would have to be the ones who'd nicknamed him "Throwback." Just because he liked poems and Earth and even ate the "clone cutlets" that the Spaceborn gang hated because they were meat, and meat-eating was a filthy Earther habit.

"The wounded world!" Others of the Spaceborn surrounded him, chanting the line he had thought was so wonderful mockingly through their noses.

The new poem was ruined now, and Mira was snatching at the others.

"Waste paper, everyone! Throwback doesn't even recycle!"

"Beggarman, beggarman!"

Jommy tried to protect his poems; but low and zero G were the

Spaceborns' particular habitats, not his. It made him dizzy if he moved too fast. They were taller than he, sinewy and taller as if freedom from constant one G let them stretch. Earth, and his shattered vision of it, watched as they danced about him.

Mira spooked him with a sudden shriek that'd get her downchecks if any teachers heard it and tore three leaves from his notebook. Then she gave him a shove that sent him flying so fast, his head spun and lunch threatened to heave itself back up.

He swallowed and tried to aim himself, use the inertia of his weightless body to crash into at least one of them and bump him into the frosty Rim bulkhead. The Spaceborn laughed and evaded him, kicking out at the last moment to send him flying in another direction. Unlike the time he'd told Andrew that his synthesizer music reminded him of spoiled tofu, this time they'd show no telltale bloodstains. Just clumsy Jommy, tripping over his own hands...and feet...and head....

"Listen to what else old Throwback says," Andrew shouted, beginning to read the poem—*his* private Earth dreams!—in an affectedly dramatic voice.

"That's so sick!" cried Mira. "He wants to live on a *dirtball!*"

The Spaceborn laughed and gasped at Mira's last word, which was about the worst thing anyone could say. If her parents heard her, they'd...they'd *talk* at her, and they were all psychs. Personally, Jommy would rather be hit. Then someone's knee caught the side of his head, and he bounced out of the sphere of jeering Spaceborn, clutching his torn papers as he caromed toward the cylinder that pierced every ring of the Habitat. Little globes of sweat flew from his forehead. The Spaceborn dodged them, shrieking with laughter.

Three Spaceborn leapt, meeting midway between deck and bulkhead to snicker and trade *dirt* stories.

"I heard there's an *Earther* here now. Came up here because he caught some sort of dirtball *disease*..."

"Earthers get all kinds of new diseases on Earth since they wiped out its ozone layer and turned the oceans to green slime..."

"Oh, *dirtballs*, that's *awful!*"

"Maybe he came up here to be with the Beggarman?"

"Or maybe to play with the Throwback."

"How 'bout it, Jommy, wanna meet the Beggarman?"

*Could you die of shame?* Jommy thought he was about to find out.

SERVICE ACCESS. He saw the words stenciled in black across a hatch twice before they made sense. Next to them was a button and, best of all, a handle, welded onto the bulkhead beside the hatch. If he could hit the button, catch the handle as he passed, and hold on while he swung round, he might escape the capering, screaming kids.

There it was, coming up.

And then he had it! The metal burned his hand as inertia tested his grip; but he hung on, then levered himself into the crawl space and watched the square of light vanish as the hatch slid shut. He saw Mira's face, scared and so pale that she looked like she was going to throw up. In zero G too. Serve them all right if she did.

He shut his eyes, squeezing them till ugly lights exploded behind his eyelids. Once the colors made him good and sick, he let his eyes open, and blinked once.

Lights the color of Luna had come on in the crawl space, each smaller than a storage disk and not so bright.

Now, where was he? Up or down? He remembered his mother's words: "Up and down are misnomers in zero G." You didn't have altitude, just attitude. Direction, he had better call it for now. What direction did he want to go in?

He wanted to go "down," toward heavier G, maybe toward the Habitat's core where he'd be his Earthside weight. The Spaceborns hated full G, so he spent whatever time he could there. He couldn't drop; there would have to be some sort of rungs.

And there they were, gleaming in the pale glow of the emergency lights. They made his skin look bleached out, except for the smears of dust and—was that blood or ink on one arm?

Why, he was actually dirty!

Dirty, bloody, driven away by the very people who ought to be his friends: what was wrong with him? Little spherical tears floated from his eyes and wet his hand. He rubbed them, leaving a clean streak. If he didn't move soon, the Spaceborn would probably call Security. And somehow, it would all be made his fault: Jommy the throwback, the dirtball—though they wouldn't use the word—going off by himself and writing poems. Jommy who couldn't take a joke or share when his classmates asked him to.

The time Andrew had given him a bloody nose, he'd raised such a howl of "Jommy's gone Beggarman" that the psychs had called them all in for family conference; and, no, his mother couldn't plead duty on the radiotelescope, and his father couldn't log in on the LAN.

"No one's been violent in our family since Breakaway," his mother had said. "And this Andrew, who you say is so well adjusted, accuses him of going Beggarman..."

"Interesting phrase," Jommy's father murmured. "Before Breakaway, I'll bet you that word was *'boogeyman.'*"

The psych glared, but not as hard as Jommy's mother. She cleared her throat.

"How will this affect Jommy's application to McAuliffe?" Dutifully his father looked up from his handheld microcomputer and asked the proper, necessary question.

It wasn't my *fault!* Jommy had wanted to howl. But his nose had throbbed, and besides, it was useless. The psych would believe Andrew, just like all the teachers always did. He was certain to make McAuliffe, the institute on the oldest Habitat where all the brightest, luckiest kids got to go. Throwback Jommy'd better say his prayers that he wasn't left behind, to miss out on advanced training and friends from all the Habitats and get stuck on makework all his life.

"He's got another year," said the psych. "If he applies himself, I think I can certify that he'd be able to deal with the stress of going off-station."

Bobbing by the ladder, Jommy gritted his teeth at the memory. *Didn't they understand?* he asked himself, as he'd asked every night since then. He *was* trying. And he *had* to get into the institute; it was his only hope of getting out of here!

*Out of here!* Jommy grabbed the nearest rung and started climbing. He was still so light that it didn't matter if he missed a couple of rungs and floated for a little. Then he felt a slight tugging, all over his body. Soon he'd be getting closer to where there was actual weight.

*Careful.* Where there was gravity, there was direction; he could fall and really hurt himself. *Fall and go squish!* he thought. Tears dripped down his face, but he needed both hands—one crumpling his papers—for the ladder. Heavier and heavier he grew, and his breath came in gasps. His hands, hot from grasping the rungs of the ladder, began to blister.

Now the rungs curved round the central bulkhead, forming a little perch beside a bigger-than-normal emergency light, shining over a hatch marked EXIT. Jommy clambered into that perch and crouched there. What was it his father had told him? "We named you Jommy for a boy in a story. He was very special and very brave." Just last year he had come across that story in his father's collection of disks. Jommy wasn't a name for someone special and brave; it was the name of a freak people chased! He'd certainly lived up to *that*, hadn't he?

He cried for a while, till he thought of Security, chasing him through the shaft.

Fear brought him fully alert. Below the EXIT marks were codes that indicated what deck and subdivision level he had reached. Just as he thought, he was near the one-G core. *Better get out.* He pressed the red button and, when the hatch hummed aside, thrust himself out into the too-bright corridor.

His timing was like everything else in his life—rotten! Wouldn't you just know he'd hear footsteps? Heavy footsteps, the steps of an adult confident of his right to go where he pleased.

The footsteps drew nearer, but there was something strange about the way they sounded. Not *thud-thud*, or even the *pad-pad* of the sure-footed Habitants; but a sort of *thud-click*, as if the someone wore metal on his feet.

The footsteps paused. Jommy knew how he must look: a dark-haired, grubby boy, clutching smeared and torn papers, crouching by an emergency hatch.

"What's this?" asked a voice he had never heard before. It was deeper, more richly accented than the Habitants'. Jommy looked down at the intruder's boots and understood why his steps had sounded so strange. Attached to the boots were small metal plates that he knew could be magnetized in low-G areas. Only one type of person would wear such boots: someone who wasn't used to low G. Someone from Earth.

Jommy had just met the Beggarman.

Even as Jommy tried to squeeze himself into the bulkhead and disappear, the Beggarman laughed.

"Why do I get the feeling I'm supposed to say 'Fee, fie, fo, fum'?" he asked. He backed up a step or two. "Get up and run, lad, if that's what you want."

The laugh and friendly words stopped Jommy in midscramble. The Earthman didn't look like the Beggarman. The Beggarman should be skeleton-thin, dressed in rags he hadn't changed since Breakaway when he'd sneaked on board the last ship to flee Earth. He should have hungry, vacant eyes. And above all, the Beggarman would never step back to let anybody run.

What Jommy saw instead was a man in late middle age, wearing the same sort of worksuit that everyone wore. But the scars of sun and gravity were upon him. Like Jommy, he was shorter than the usual Habitant. His hair was streaked with gray. His skin was wrinkled and darker—*tanned*, the word was—and his eyes, under thick, thick eyebrows, were very bright.

"You were expecting...what? Some sort of monster? Instead, you met me. Sorry to disappoint you. Dr. George I. Stewart, at your service," said the Earthman. "The I's for Isherwood; my father had a strange sense of humor. Want a hand?"

Jommy shook his head and braced himself against the wall, his free hand patting the dust from his sides and backside.

"Care to tell me your name?"

The Privacy Codes said you didn't have to give your name. You didn't even have to be nice if you thought you were in trouble. Just step out into the corridor and call the nearest Security Monitor for help. But would the real Beggarman give his name, even make a little joke out of it, then spread out his hands to show he meant no harm?

Tentatively Jommy smiled back. The man didn't look as if he were going to—what was the bad Earther word?—*mug* Jommy.

"I'm Jommy," he told the Earther at last, feeling awful even as he said it. He'd had the same feeling the first time he'd taken free-fall drill. Only that time he'd thrown up.

"Maybe you'll tell me your last name later. It couldn't be 'Cross' by any chance, could it?"

Jommy grinned. That was the name of his name-sake in the book *Slan*. The Earther grinned back, an I-didn't-think-so-either sort of smile. Oh, Jommy hoped the Spaceborn were lying about Earthers.

"Well, we're both named for loners. And I'd say, young Jommy, that we're both pretty far from where we're supposed to be. If this were my home, I'd guess you'd been in quite a fight. Who won?"

Jommy let his wad of papers fall. By now Mira had probably cried all over her parents and told them some sort of awful story. He'd *never* get into the McAuliffe now; he'd be stuck here forever, a disappointment to his parents and a bad example for the little kids.

This George Stewart man stopped and picked up the paper, began to read. Flick...flick...his eyes went, like a scanner trained on computers just like they had on the Habitat. He raised an eyebrow.

"No-oo!" Jommy darted at him. It was the Spaceborn all over again, stealing and jeering at his poems.

"Steady there!" Stewart said, smoothed out the papers, and returned them. "Some of these lines are really good. I especially liked the one about the 'wounded world.' That's precisely what we're doing on Earth, you know. Healing it. Making it a garden again."

Jommy slid to a stop. "They *are*? I mean, you *are* healing Earth? I mean, you like my poems?" The questions tumbled out as untidy as his room until breathlessness made him stop. He gasped for air and indig-nation, finishing with "Why are you reading my stuff?"

"Were you fighting to protect them?" asked the Earthman.

"They're *private*!" Jommy said.

"And someone grabbed them. Probably started reading them to someone else. And you only wanted to crawl into a hole and pull it in after you, right?"

"That's just what I did!" Jommy admitted. "Climbed down from the Rim in a maintenance shaft."

"Did you ever come that way before?" Dr. Stewart looked genuine-ly impressed. "I wouldn't want to take that climb in the near dark. Not to mention the low G. It still makes me sick. Nice going."

Somehow, Jommy found himself walking alongside the Earthman, describing his escape routes. "Most of them lead to full G," he finished up. "The Spaceborn don't come down here much, but I do."

They passed a washroom. At that moment, Jommy would have traded any hope he'd ever had of the McAuliffe for a chance to go in and wash. What if this stranger followed him inside? It wouldn't be Jommy's fault, but who'd believe him?

The Earthman leaned against the bulkhead. "You look like you found every speck of dust in that whole crawlway. Go wash. I'll wait outside."

◆ ◆ ◆

A squirt of recycled water and a chemical towel could do wonders, Jommy thought as he marched outside. He felt better now; he could be brave and well adjusted now. And then Dr. Stewart cocked his head at him and looked at him, *really* looked, the way the psychs did just before things got more uncomfortable than usual.

"I wonder," he began, and Jommy chilled. As if Dr. Stewart could actually read him like his own poems, he smiled slightly, reassuringly. "No, I'm not going to break Privacy. Believe it or not, we do learn man-ners on Earth. Even respect for other people's rules. About these Spaceborn—sounds like they've been on your back…"

Jommy looked blank.

"I mean, teasing you for quite some time. Now, I'd be the last per-son to say I understood Habitant customs, but don't you have rules about harassment? Seems to me that what they're doing violates those rules."

Jommy's face flushed, and he felt himself scrunching up as if someone had tried to hit him.

"You think I'd *tell*?" he demanded in a rush of anger that left him feeling deflated, yet lighter than he'd felt in months. "You know what happens when you tell? They talk at you for hours: talk, talk, talk. You really think they'd believe *me*? The Spaceborn are the most popular kids in class. I'd just be Jommy the throwback, Jommy the freak, trying to get attention. Jommy the *squealing* freak."

"Jommy Cross wasn't a freak."

"Yeah? Then why'd he have those antennae? And what would *you* call a slan?"

"I'd call him the sort of man who helps heal his society."

Ignoring the Earther's answer, Jommy spat the words out with loathing. "Now I'll never get into the McAuliffe Institute, never get off this...this..." To his horror, his eyes were filling and his voice was shaking, so he made sure to say the worst thing he could. "This filthy *dirtball!*"

And now he was going to cry, and this Dr. Stewart would report him for maladjustment. A hand touched his arm, and Jommy tensed. "I'm not Beg...I mean crazy!" he protested. Every Habitant knew that outbursts of temper led to Beggarman behavior.

"Of course you're not," said Dr. Stewart. He looked as if he wanted to hug Jommy, but then he glanced up, saw the red light of the Security Monitor, and let his hand drop. "You've got a right to feel bad and let it out. There's nothing wrong with you but your choice of cursewords. 'Filthy dirtball' indeed—as if dirt were something bad. Come with me, Jommy. *I'll* show you dirt. I'll show you *real* dirt!"

He started down the corridor so rapidly that Jommy broke into a scamper to keep up. He dashed tears from his cheeks with both hands just in time to see Dr. Stewart lay his palm against a lock above which was stenciled HYDROPONICS (backup). The door slid aside with a *whoosh* and a rush of warm, fragrant air, and the Earthman led the way in.

Jommy paused at the entrance. Already sticky, he'd have paid hard money—assuming he owned any—to escape this visit to hydro. He hated hydro and the time that every kid had to put in on it. Hydro was hot; hydro was sticky; and, rather than ruin clothing that had to be recycled, you had to work bare. The Spaceborn always teased him. *"What's that pouch round Jommy's waist?" "What waist?" "Oh, that's just his stomach." "When's the baby due?"*

Still, he supposed he'd better be polite.

Now Dr. Stewart was standing by what had to be the strangest-looking hydro tank Jommy had ever seen, and he was grinning as if he dared Jommy to follow.

*If he tells me it's for my own good, I'm out of here*, Jommy promised himself. Instead, Dr. Stewart stuck his hand in the tank and brought it up. Jommy winced: Contaminating hydro was about as low as you could get.

But no nutrient solutions dripped from the Earthman's hand. Instead, he held out clumps of crumbling brownish-black stuff, which he allowed to rain back into the tank.

"What's *that?*" Jommy asked.

"*That,* my boy, is *earth*. Honest-to-goodness, brought-from-the-homeworld *dirt*. If you want to be polite, you can call it *soil*. It works like the hydroponics solutions. Like it?"

Jommy shook his head no, yet found himself drawn to the tub of earth. The lattices of the carrot greens were oddly dark and squat; the tomato plants huddled close to the surface of the...the *soil*. There were rows and rows of curiously vivid plants, all smaller than they should be, and all a bright green.

"They're so *short*!" Jommy muttered. "Not like hydro on H-deck at all."

"Those spindly mutants?" Dr. Stewart challenged him. "You let a plant grow in one-quarter G, and spindly is what you get. I've got a tank up there as a control group. Plants weren't made to shoot up like that."

Jommy knew what was right to say: Plants weren't made to be dosed with pesticide till they poisoned the very folk who ate them either.

"Come on, boy," said Dr. Stewart. Jommy noticed that the door had not yet closed and felt reassured.

He crept toward the tank and, at Dr. Stewart's nod, touched the black soil. It was moist and warm from the lights overhead. He picked it up, sniffed at it.

"That's one sort of soil. We've got loam, chalky soil, peaty soil—different soils for different parts of the world. They all smell different; all *taste* different, I've been told, though I can't bring myself to try it. And we're bringing them all back."

"Healing the ecosystem?" In his earliest lessons, Jommy had learned to revere the ecosystem and learned also how Earth had destroyed its own balance of nature.

"Don't call it an ecosystem, boy. Call it a world. A home!" Stewart's voice was so rich that Jommy realized that the man was homesick for that glowing blue world that hung in the black sky.

"This is home," Jommy said.

"This is a *habitat*," said Stewart. "One asteroid, though, and all it would be is a former habitat. One longer-than-normal solar flare, and you'd all be cowering in shelters, doing genetic testing, and worrying how many eyes your grandchildren might have. Earth, now, Earth is a home, a home world that can recover if an asteroid hits it or a solar flare strikes. As it's doing right now."

"You *like* Earth?" Jommy had wanted things without hope for too long not to recognize longing when he heard it.

"Boy, do I miss it."

"I wouldn't miss *here*," Jommy admitted.

The Earthman smiled. "I could tell you about Earth, if you liked. If your parents agreed."

Jommy put his hands firmly behind his back. "Why?"

"A bargain. Maybe I need help."

Jommy raised his eyebrows as he'd once seen a teacher do at a particularly obvious excuse.

"Look at this!" The Earthman pulled up a carrot and held it out to Jommy.

"You'll waste it!" Jommy yelped.

Stewart shook his head, wiped off the carrot—more brightly orange than any Jommy had ever seen, and grinning at Jommy's shock, bit into it. Surely no vegetable ever made such a satisfying crunch.

"Want one?" Stewart asked, with his mouth full. His bad manners were reassuring, but Jommy shook his head. The idea of eating something that had grown in actual dirt made his mouth water the way it did in zero G or just before he got sick.

"Next time," Stewart muttered. "Or go on up to hydro and try one of the carrots like you're used to. Then come back and eat one of these. Test them. In fact..." He eyed Jommy with such obvious speculation that the boy laughed.

"Much as I like it, I'm only a part-time gardener."

*What do you do?* It was a breach of Privacy to ask, so Jommy didn't.

"Here's the bargain. I tell you about Earth. In return, I could use someone to help me with my plants. Measure the growth of plants at Earth G against those raised in low G. Test vitamin content, taste: that sort of thing. Keep good records, then write them up. What do you think?"

*I hate hydroponics.* Jommy almost blurted it out.

The Earthman was watching him with a not-quite-grin. "Not a gardener, are you?"

Jommy shrugged. What if he did tend some plants and make some notes? He knew he could write up a good report—and after the day's episode with the Spaceborn, he knew he'd never have the nerve to read "Earth Dreams" to anyone, much less submit his poems to the McAuliffe. Besides, he could keep his coverall on, and there wouldn't be any girls around to giggle at him. And besides that, being enthusiastic about vegetables and nutrition was considered very well adjusted. It beat growing crystals or writing synthesizer music that made your eyeballs ache to listen to it—like some of the Spaceborn did—and it would look great on the McAuliffe application.

◆ ◆ ◆

The next day, Jommy had begun carefully to weed plants when Dr. Stewart came in with a package.

"Do you like music?" he asked, waving an iridescent disk at the boy.

"Not like Andrew writes. It makes my eyes ache."

"Try this," the Earthman said, and fitted the disk into the player he had brought. Waterfalls of sound poured over Jommy: triumphant horns lifting above a steady current of strings and a bedrock of drums.

"That's not synthesized," Stewart told him. "Every note comes from human breath, wood, gut"—Jommy grimaced—"and human talent, not chance or programming. This is old-style music. Earth music."

The music slowed, rang out over the drumbeats. Abruptly it stopped. "Here," said Dr. Stewart, "see for yourself." He lifted the disk, pretended to toss it to Jommy, who protested with an upheld, dirty hand. *To the New World* read the label.

"Why'd I bring it?" asked the Earthman. "They say plants like music. You can test it: Dvorak on one group and computer-synthesized squawks on another."

Then he was gone. The disk shone temptingly, its light shimmering as the door slid shut. Hastily Jommy scrubbed his hands, fitted disk into player, and let the triumphant horns surge over him. It was a wonder, he thought, that the plants did not rustle in time with it.

◆ ◆ ◆

Weeks later into what Dr. Stewart called the growing season, Jommy hurried into hydro. Quickly he turned on the tapes, then began his day's work. Counting, weighing, and measuring went rapidly, now that he was used to it. Quickly and meticulously, he entered his results in his database.

◆ ◆ ◆

"Elegant programming, Jommy," Jommy's Comp Sci teacher told the class. He looked as surprised at what he was saying as the Spaceborn. "I imagine that your database must be really easy to use."

Jommy ducked his head. He used to struggle just to make his teachers focus on him, not get that glazed-over look in their eyes before they called on someone more prestigious.

Two or three of the Spaceborn glared at him. "He thinks he's so great," Andrew grumbled.

"Now, Andrew, you're much too well adjusted to sink to jealousy. Don't you know how it can poison your thoughts?"

Jommy tuned out on what sounded like the sort of helpful, well-meant lecture on cooperation that had always made him squirm with humiliation.

Andrew only grimaced. With his mind on his plants and his music, Jommy was surprised how little pleasure that gave him. If Andrew was in trouble, it would probably be for the first and last time.

I'll *get* you, dirtball, Andrew mouthed, and Jommy knew he, too, was in trouble. Again. When class ended, he scuttled out, making himself small, so small he overheard his teacher talking to a friend.

"Jommy's database was a first-rate piece of work," the Comp Sci teacher said. "Tell you frankly, I didn't think that he had it in him. He's always been sort of an underachieving lump. Now it turns out he's simply a late bloomer."

The friend muttered something about the psychs and tin gods. Both teachers laughed.

"He doesn't let it go to his head," Jommy heard his teacher say.

That couldn't be the old Throwback the teacher was talking about, could it?

◆ ◆ ◆

"You programmed this?" his father said that evening. For once Jommy hadn't had to compete with the terminal for his father's attention. Both of them were bent over it, testing Jommy's work.

"This is excellent," he approved, just as Jommy's mother walked into the main room.

"What is?" she asked.

"Program our Jommy wrote."

*Our Jommy.* His eyes filled with tears. His mother bent over him, kissed his hair, then turned her eyes to the screen.

"He's better at it than I am," she said. "That's not hard. But I can still tell fine work from a kludge. Anyone mind if we order from Central Kitchen? I know it's my turn to cook, but I need to get back to the observatory. We'll need the extra credits to equip you for McAuliffe, Jommy. I won't have you in class with my old teachers looking like something that even the Beggarman would throw away."

◆ ◆ ◆

Getting the approval he'd always wanted was great, but what Jommy mostly heard was the music of horns and strings, and Dr. Stewart's voice, telling him of Earth. His stories made what had been dry tapes on geology or ecology come alive—and his teachers' smiles became beams. The music of Earth had fully caught him now. The sound was a river, sweeping him along, occasionally tossing him into side eddies as he caromed off a bulkhead in low G.

"Slow down!" Dr. Stewart cried. The Earthman was unsteady in the low G, squeamish about entering weightlessness, which he remembered with loathing from the trip from Earth to the Habitat. Jommy was surprised how easy it was to help him. The practice he was getting in switching grav levels made him very sure, just as his time in the one-G hydro lab was making him strong. He didn't even think of laughing. Instead, throughout the trip to the Rim, whenever Dr. Stewart asked him to slow, Jommy would bound back to help him.

"I feel like an injured old man," grumbled the Earthman. He swallowed, his face turning slightly green.

Jommy knew those signs. If Dr. Stewart was sick here, there would be a terrible mess to clean.

"Look around you," he urged. "Listen. Even now, there are people up here, playing zero-G volleyball. There's a whir—someone must be in the minimills. You know, we manufacture equipment here and send it back to Earth."

"Ball bearings, medical supplies, and semiconductors," agreed Dr. Stewart. He looked around, more curious now than sick.

Jommy sighed with relief, but continued. "We always have to keep a lookout. You know, you tell me that Earth is safe, Earth heals, that there's room for mistakes on Earth. That sounds good to me, because here we don't dare make any mistakes. Not with vacuum outside."

"Sounds risky," said Dr. Stewart, in a tone that meant "just teasing."

"So does Earth," Jommy retorted. "Still, we're all managing, aren't we?"

He knew he sounded obnoxious, like the Spaceborn, lecturing Dr. Stewart. But the man just grinned.

"Streetwise," he said, and Jommy looked puzzled. "That's a survival mechanism. Somehow, just as you said, we muddle through. And Earth abides."

Jommy looked up at him. Stewart's words sounded like Privacy subjects, but if Jommy didn't ask, he might burst.

"Earth abides?" Stewart repeated, making it a question. "It's the truth. But it's also the name of a book. Maybe you'd like to read it one day."

Jommy could see his parents' faces. *"Where did you get this, Jommy?"* *"The Beggarman gave it to me."*

"We're almost at the Rim," Jommy assured him. "You're doing fine."

Jommy floated through the last pressure door, unsealing it and making certain that Stewart bobbed past before it could close, and the Earthman muttered something about role reversal. But he chuckled while he said it.

"What I do for my work," he said.

Now that was too good a chance to pass up.

"What *do* you do back...home?" Jommy asked. Maybe they were good enough friends now that asking wouldn't violate Privacy.

"I touch the future."

"That's the McAuliffe Institute's motto," the boy said. "Are you a teacher?"

Dr. Stewart looked thoughtful. "On Earth we're all teachers," he said. "Let me tell you a story about a wise man. He once said that all you need for a school...wait a second, slow down!...was a log and two people sitting on either end."

Jommy thought of his Habitat's learning skills center, the labs and the computers and the fiber-optics workshops, not to mention the psychs. It would be nice to sit on a log—whatever that was—with someone like Dr. Stewart and just listen.

"And you know what, Jommy? The good thing about that sort of school is that if you're really poor, you can do without the log!"

"We're almost here." Jommy waited for Dr. Stewart to finish his story. "One more lock." They bobbed in the no gravity as they neared the heavy door. With a flourish, he palmed the viewport lock. He heard a deep intake of breath and reached around for the hand-held suction pump mounted next to the oxygen on the bulkhead.

But Dr. Stewart didn't look like he was going to be sick. Instead, he held out his palm, as if to touch the gleaming, distant world. The wounded world.

"Dear Earth, I do salute thee with my hand," he murmured.

Jommy wondered at the language. It had the rhythm of music. Dr. Stewart sounded like one of the tapes of the classics that only teachers ever listened to. The Earthman blinked fast, but not before a tear floated away from his face.

Then Jommy thought he heard a rustle, the snick of a lock being released. He spun around...

Too fast. Inertia flung him against the bulkhead, and Dr. Stewart laughed. Jommy was surprised that it didn't hurt when Dr. Stewart laughed at him.

"What did you say about being careful?" he asked, and they both laughed again. A minute later Dr. Stewart was pointing out Earth's continents on the tiny, brilliant globe.

They didn't mention the sounds again.

◆ ◆ ◆

Jommy swung down the corridor in one-G country toward his hydro lab. It would take him ten more steps, he guessed, to go from the lift to the door. He was growing fast. At the start of his experiments, it used to take him fifteen. He walked fast, not noticing the bleakness of the corridors. Few of the Spaceborn cared to venture down to full G, so no one decorated bulkheads that few would see and admire. Soundproofing was good down here, but even now, Jommy ought to be able to hear the music that he kept on for his plants.

They reacted well to old Earth music like Dvorak and Bach, who wrote in patterns more intricate than a computer program. But plants that had to listen to a tape of Andrew's music that Jommy'd "borrowed" from school tended to shrivel and wilt. Still, he couldn't write "thrived to Bach" and "shriveled and wilted because of synthesizer music" in his report without backing up his claims. The McAuliffe applications and references were due in a few days.

Then the music boomed, and something else—within the lab—boomed too. Jommy flattened himself against the corridor, trying to walk without sound in the full gravity, and glad that he was used to it. A crash, muffled by the drums, followed the boom.

Jommy darted for the nearest service access, flung himself through the hatch, and grunted when it proved to be a tight fit.

Time got tight too, as the hydro door *whoosh*ed open, releasing music and whispers into the corridor. Then the music died, and someone giggled. In the cleanliness of the maintenance shaft, Jommy could smell the green earth scents he had come to love.

Three of the Spaceborn—Andrew, Mira, and Chris—ran out. Or they would have run if they hadn't had to stop every few steps and moan about their aching backs and legs. They left brown footprints, as if they'd been stepping in soil.

"Oh, *no!*" Jommy whispered. He slid out of the service hatch and ran for hydro as fast as if this were shelter drill.

When he got to the door, he stopped. The place looked like a meteor had hit. Tubs were overturned, and dirt and the clear hydro solution had blended into a horrible muck. His plants lay plucked and scattered across the filthy floor. Computer's lights were on—no one would ever deliberately crash a system—but a glance across the room at it told Jommy that his database had been wiped. And the disk that had held so much music lay scratched and bent.

His experiments. His plants. His report. His music.

"Those dirtballs," Jommy said quietly.

Then the tears came, and he scrubbed at them with one dirty hand.

"Dirtballs!" he shouted.

Sense would be to call Security. Sense would be to find his teachers or his parents or Dr. Stewart. Abandoning sense, Jommy tracked the Spaceborn by their dirty footprints down the corridor to the lift.

Seeing his face, Mira backed off. Andrew tried to run, but he was slow and awkward in the one G. Chris, who had always been a sneak, stuck out a grimy boot. It caught between Jommy's feet and he went over. In the last moment before he sprawled, he wrenched his body around so he toppled into Andrew. Andrew, Chris, and Jommy crashed onto the floor, grunting, punching, and kicking, while Mira shrieked at the Security Monitor.

"Jommy's gone Beggarman," she reported, tears in her sweet, earnest voice. "Oh! Andrew's nose is bleeding. Jommy hit him."

And hit him again and again. They had destroyed his lab. They had destroyed his work. They'd made him disappoint his friend. This was worse than it had been months ago, before he met Dr. Stewart, because now he had hoped, he had so hoped...

Tears blinded his eyes, and Andrew got in a lucky punch. Jommy yelled with pain and outrage, and punched back hard.

◆ ◆ ◆

Trankspray filled the air. Even as Jommy felt himself going limp, he borrowed a description of the mist from one of Dr. Stewart's stories: cool and sweet as a summer's evening. Everyone went suddenly quiet.

Under the influence of the spray, Jommy found himself thinking clearly. Maybe things weren't so bad. Tubs could be turned upright, plants replanted, floors scrubbed—and his data were backed up. "There are only two kinds of users," his father had always said. "Happy users, and fools who don't download."

"We just wanted to see his plants," Mira was saying in a terrified whine, "but he threw over the tubs and chased us down the corridor. We tried to get away, but he tackled Andrew and Chris!"

"What a lie," Jommy said, disgusted, through lips that felt rubbery. "They couldn't run in full G. I watched them wreck my lab..." To his shame, his voice broke.

"Throwback," crooned Andrew, and then Jommy knew the worst of it. No one would believe him. They would all think he had gone Beggarman.

*Beggarman*, Jommy thought as boots clattered down the corridor, the long, unsteady footsteps of Habitants unused to one G, the shorter, firmer strides of...

"Dr. Stewart!" he tried to shout. It came out a croak.

The Earthman reached Jommy about the same time as his parents.

"What happened?" Three voices asked at once.

"They wrecked the lab," Jommy said. "I bet the one at one-quarter G is smashed too."

"Why would Andrew, Chris, and Mira wreck your lab experiments?" a teacher who had never liked Jommy much asked. "You've never been especially good neighbors with them, but they're well-adjusted children; they wouldn't do something like that."

A Security woman spoke into her wristcom in an undertone. "He's right," she confirmed. "The lab in the one-quarter-G complex has been vandalized."

Jommy moaned. He'd never get into McAuliffe. Worse than that, he would probably be sent to the psychs until he was as old as Earth. To his astonishment, bloody as he was, his mother put her arms around him.

"Why didn't you tell us you weren't happy?" she asked, her face twisting like Mira's, as if she were going to cry too. "Whatever it is, Jommy. It doesn't matter. Just get well!"

*I didn't do it!* Jommy thought, furious. He wanted to break away from the wrangle of adults, but the trankspray made him feel as if he'd been running through two G. Maybe three.

"Wait a moment," said Dr. Stewart. No one but Jommy heard him.

*"Listen to me!"* boomed the Earthman, and everyone started.

"There's truth in dirt," he said. "Look at the children's boots. Now, if Jommy had overturned his own plant tubs, he'd have gotten his boots dirty. But look at his feet. He's picked up some of the dirt on the floor, but it hasn't been ground into his boot soles. Now, look at the other three. Go on, look at them!"

To Jommy's surprise, the Security officers obeyed as if they had been preschoolers.

"Rubbed in, right?" said Stewart.

The Security people nodded.

"Give me the comm," said Dr. Stewart. "Hartley?"

Could he mean Chief Counselor Hartley? Could he call her just like that? Other people had to make appointments to see her, and call her by titles, but Dr. Stewart treated her just like he treated Jommy.

Hartley's voice, known throughout the network of Habitats, replied. "What is it, Mr. Minister?"

"Can you come down to one G? We've had some sabotage," said Dr. Stewart. "Involving the people I told you about. I'd say it's important."

"On my way," said the chief counselor.

♦ ♦ ♦

Chief Counselor Hartley arrived in full G with one hand pressed to the small of her back. She was tall, thin, and almost eight months pregnant.

"Counselor," Dr. Stewart said, ducking his head in what Jommy realized had to be an old-fashioned bow, "my sincere regrets at dragging you down here. Someone bring Counselor Hartley a chair!"

Jommy's father was the first to comply. Dr. Stewart made a little ceremony of seating the counselor. She tried to protest, but sighed with relief as she sank down.

Seeing the counselor had taken the words out of Jommy's mouth, but not for long. Just as he opened his mouth, his mother pressed his shoulder to silence him.

*"Mr. Minister?"* his mother asked, in the special tone she kept for faulty data.

"Earth's Minister of Education," said Counselor Hartley.

So his Dr. Stewart *had* been a teacher once, after all. Jommy sagged more with relief than from the trankspray; he hadn't been lied to.

Questions erupted from three sets of parents—Andrew's, Mira's, and Chris's—from Security, and very feebly, from Jommy himself.

Dr. Stewart held up a hand. "We've got a case of sabotage," he said. "This young man did a pretty professional job on some lab work for me—Jommy, do you have a backup on your data?"

Jommy nodded.

"Apparently, some of his classmates decided to break up the place a little. And Jommy—well, he caught them at it, and lost his temper."

"Lost his temper!" one of Mira's fathers shouted, though Jommy noted that he never moved from where he stood. "Went Beggarman and *hit* people."

That caused a muttering: violence, the threat of Earth-style violence, which the Habitat was built to escape from. And Jommy had revived it.

*Kiss McAuliffe good-bye,* he told himself. But he had known that all along.

"Counselor," said Dr. Stewart, Mr. Minister Stewart, the old trickster, "if you look at the children's shoes, you can see who was in the lab and who wasn't."

The woman nodded. "Highly antisocial," she said.

The Spaceborns' parents shrank: antisocial tendencies meant downchecks on their records and psych sessions all around.

Jommy almost grinned, but "Quiet, you!" growled Dr. Stewart. Jommy's mother's hand tightened on his shoulder.

"And what of our son?" she asked.

"I know you had plans for him. The McAuliffe, I believe?"

What else was there? You went to McAuliffe or you went nowhere all your life. McAuliffe would never take a boy who'd gone Beggarman.

His mother nodded. "But this violence!" Her hand shook for a moment, then steadied. "I don't know where he learned it, but he's our son, and we'll see him through this."

That meant the psychs and therapy. Medicines, probably, and re-education. Jommy shut his eyes and stifled a groan.

"Not precisely," said Dr. Stewart. "You may have guessed that I take an interest in the boy."

Jommy's father started forward, his face red as Jommy had never seen it.

Counselor Hartley held up a hand. "I was aware of this. When the minister arrived here, he told me he would be visiting each habitat, looking for young people who were failing to thrive..."

"'A bad fit' were the words I used," put in Dr. Stewart.

"You make my son sound like he's some sort of freak." Jommy's father clenched his fists.

"I see where he gets his urge to violence," remarked Dr. Stewart. "I don't think Jommy is a freak at all. On the contrary. He's stood up well under abuse, worked hard. And he was very kind, despite a highly prejudiced upbringing"—Dr. Stewart grinned at the sensation *that* caused—"to a stranger, even to the point of mastering his dislike of zero G. My ministry is looking for boys and girls like Jommy who don't fit on their habitats, who show signs that they might adapt to Earth."

"I'm not letting my son go live on a dirtball," Jommy's mother burst out.

"What do you want him to do? Squeeze into McAuliffe and hate every minute of it? Or not go, and wind up—with his talents—doing maintenance?" Stewart snapped. "I'm offering Jommy a ride to Earth, training there, a chance to be one of the first generation of people who can live on a planet *or* in space. Oh, he'll go to the McAuliffe, all right. Later on, as an instructor, to teach the less flexible kids. To heal the angers and misunderstandings since the Breakaway. To heal the split that's grown up between planet and habitat, Earthborn and Spaceborn."

"And, if we ever, ever manage to escape this solar system, it'll be people like Jommy we'll need on the ships. I had a reason for setting him the experiment I did. You've been growing hothouse plants up here. I think we need something hardier."

Jommy sighed. It was all he could manage.

"Well, Jommy, what do you think?" Stewart spoke to him, not to the adults. "Ready to leave the greenhouse?"

"For the greenhouse effect?" The words leapt out before he could stop them, but Dr. Stewart was too important for people to scold Jommy in his presence. Suddenly Jommy yawned. Stupid trank was making him sleepy.

"We've got the greenhouse effect under control. But don't worry. We've got other problems you can sink your teeth into." Stewart grinned again, and Jommy grinned back.

◆ ◆ ◆

Jommy's arm still itched from immunizations, but he couldn't scratch. His pressure suit was too thick, and, besides, he was strapped into his couch, waiting for the faint bump that meant that the Earth shuttle had left the Habitat, had left home. Though zero G no longer troubled him, he swallowed hard.

He was on his way to Earth!

"You'll have to work hard and justify the minister's trust," people had been lecturing him since his future had suddenly met him in a mud-tracked corridor. And Jommy had nodded gravely and fought off grins as he remembered Dr. Stewart's last comments. "First, I was the Beggarman. Now I'm Mr. Minister. You shouldn't even *talk* to the Beggarman, but it's fine, of course, if Mr. Minister gives you a going-away gift. So, here."

It wasn't a disk or a tape, but a real book with *Earth Abides* stamped in worn gold on the fraying cover.

Never mind his baggage allowance. He left out one pair of boots that would probably not be heavy enough anyway and packed Dr. Stewart's gift instead.

There came the bump. For a minute, panic gripped him. Then the shuttle turned, and an image of Earth appeared on its screens. The music of Earth, strings, horns, and drums calling him to a new world, rose in his imagination. He was going home.

# Rich Man, Poor Man

♦ ♦ ♦

## AN AKAMBA TALE, RETOLD BY ROGER D. ABRAHAMS

It happened one time, long, long ago, that in one of the villages of the *Akamba*, there were two men who lived as neighbors. One was rich, and the other was poor, but they were friends. The poor man worked for the rich man, helping him. Now a famine came to the land. And when the suffering became very severe, the rich man forgot the poor man, and the poor man who used to eat at his friend's house now had to beg from him. Finally, the rich man chased him away altogether, because a rich man cannot remain a friend of a poor person for too long, and he felt that even the scraps he now gave his poor neighbor were just too much.

One day, this poor man was scrounging about in the village for something to eat. He was given maize by a man who took pity on him, and he took it home to his wife, and she cooked it. But they had no meat with which to make it into soup; nor did they have salt with which to season it. So the man said, "I will go to see if my rich friend is having a good soup tonight." He went and found that the meal cooking there gave out a nice, sweet smell. So he returned back to his house, got the cooked maize, and brought it back to the rich man's house, where he sat against the wall and ate it, breathing in the smell that came from the rich man's meal. When he had eaten, he returned to his own home.

Another day, the poor man saw the rich man and went up to him and said, "I came a few days ago, while you were eating your food, and I sat by the wall, and ate my food together with the delicious smell that came from your food."

The rich man was furious, and he said, "So that's why my food was completely tasteless that day! It was you who ate the good taste from my food, and you must pay me for it! I'm taking you to the judge to file a case against you." And he did that, and the poor man was told to pay one goat to the rich man for eating the sweet smell from his food. But the poor man could not afford even one goat, and he broke down and cried as he went back to his house.

On his way home, he met a wise man and speechmaker, and he told him what had happened. The wise man gave him a goat, and told him to keep that goat until he came back. Now, the judge had appointed a certain day when the poor man was to pay the rich man; and on that day, many people came together to witness the payment. The wise man came also, and when he saw the people talking, he asked, "Why are you making so much fuss here?" The judge said, "This poor man is supposed to pay this rich man a goat, for the smell he breathed from the rich man's food." The wise man asked his first question again, and he was given the same answer. So the wise man said, "Will you let me give another judgement on this case?" The people said, "Yes, if you are a good judge!" So he went on to say, "A man who steals must give back only as much as he has taken, no more, no less."

When the people asked him how he could pay back just the smell of good food, the wise man replied, "I will show you!" Then he turned to the rich man, and said to him, "Rich man, I am going to hit this goat, and when it bleats, I want you to take its bleating sound! You are not to touch this poor man's goat, unless he touched your food." Then he said again to the people, "Listen now, while I pay back the rich man." So he hit the goat and it bleated, and he said to the rich man, "Take that sound as payment for the smell of your good food!"

# Project Report

♦ ♦ ♦

**BY JOHN COUTTS**

*A dramatic poem*

. . . . . . . . . . . . . . . . . . . . . . . . . . . . . . . . . . . . .

*(A missionary working in Lagos, Nigeria, received a grant to provide Christmas cheer for old people. He helped to share the gifts and received an unexpected blessing. He is recording on tape a report explaining how the grant was spent.)*

SPEAKER: "To Projects Officer, P.O. Box, etcetera:

Dear Sir:

      The grant you gave was used as follows:
We purchased thirty plastic bags. In each
We placed a pound of rice, some tea, dried beans,
St. Matthew's gospel in the local language,
Sugar and salt, a box of matches, tinned
Tomato puree, local leaves resembling
Spinach, bananas, oranges, some palm
Oil, and a greeting card"

                New paragraph.

      "The funds, we trust were wisely spent; the list
Of aged people checked and double-checked
In case of fraud. The bags were packed on Christmas
Eve, and taken round by volunteers
On Christmas Day. Each team included one
At least who spoke the local language. I
Myself took part..."

*(The speaker stops dictating and starts remembering.)*

Old woman, please forgive.

We came to help. I never knew your home
Was bare, so very bare; the walls unpainted
Concrete: never thought we'd scare you stiff,
We strangers bearing gifts. You saw and dreaded
My whitish face and khaki shorts, my thin
Thin lips and pointed nose. Was it police?
Or Taxmen? Trouble — yes, official trouble!
We gave you such a fright on Christmas morning
Attempting to deliver one of thirty
Plastic bags containing...never mind...
For once you understood, you offered thanks
In long melodious words and solemn gestures
Centuries old. You greeted Khaki Shorts
(Who hardly knows the local language) kindly,
Maternally, a queen beside your charcoal
Fire: then you smiled and made your farewell curtsey
Slowly and gently, being old, but smoothly,
As though the years had spared your maidenhood.
You blessed me then. We went our way unsnubbed
And you unpatronized.

                    Let's try again.

*(And so back to the dictation)*

"To Projects Officer, P.O. Box, etcetera:

Dear Sir,

         The grant you gave was used as follows..."

# People From Mars

◆ ◆ ◆

**BY**

**HELENA
NORBERG-HODGE**

*At one village I witnessed a trekking group armed with cameras, bon bons, and pens, virtually attack the villagers. Dressed in fluorescent greens, reds, and blues, they poked their cameras in unsuspecting faces without a word and then moved on to their next victim.*

— Angry tourist, 1990

I magine living your day-to-day life as usual and suddenly waking up to find your town invaded by people from another planet. Speaking a strange tongue and looking even stranger, these extraterrestrials lead quite extraordinary lives. They do not appear to know what work is, but enjoy constant leisure. Moreover, they have special powers and inexhaustible wealth.

Imagine further how your children might react to this experience, how fascinated they would be. Just think how difficult it would be to stop them from following these creatures, to convince them that they were better off staying home with you. How could you prevent impressionable teenagers, in their search for identity, from being swept off their feet?

I was in Ladakh from the time tourism started, and was able to observe the process of change from the beginning. Since I spoke the language fluently, I gained an insight into the intense psychological pressures that modernization brings. Looking at the modern world from something of a Ladakh perspective, I also became aware that our culture looks infinitely more successful from the outside than we experience it on the inside.

With no warning, people from another world descended on Ladakh. Each day many would spend as much as a hundred dollars, an amount roughly equivalent to someone spending fifty thousand dollars a day in America. In the traditional subsistence economy, money played a minor role, used primarily for luxuries — jewelry, silver, and gold. Basic needs — food, clothing, and shelter — were provided for without money. The labor one needed was free of charge, part of an intricate web of human relationships.

In one day a tourist would spend the same amount that a Ladakhi family might in a year. Ladakhis did not realize that money played a completely different role for the foreigners; that back home they needed it to survive; that food, clothing, and shelter all cost money — a lot of money. Compared to these strangers, they sudddenly felt poor. During my first years in Ladakh, young children I had never seen before used to run up to me and press apricots into my hands. Now little figures, looking shabbily Dickensian in threadbare Western clothing, greet foreigners with an empty outstretched hand. They demand, "one pen, one pen," a phrase that has become the new mantra of Ladakhi children.

The tourists, for their part, think Ladakhis are backward. The few who experience the hospitality of a village home invariably speak of this as the highlight of their holiday. But most of them can only see Ladakhi culture from the outside, and they view it out of the experience of their own culture and economy. They assume that money plays the same role in Ladakh as at home. If they meet a Ladakhi who is earning only two dollars a day, they are horrified and show it. Implicitly or explicitly, they say to him, "Oh, you poor thing, I'd better give you a big tip." To Western eyes, Ladakhis look poor. Tourists can only see the material side of the culture — worn-out woolen robes, the *dzo* pulling a plough, the barren land. They cannot see peace of mind or the quality of family and community relations. They cannot see the psychological, social, and spiritual wealth of the Ladakhis.

Besides giving the illusion that all Westerners are multimillionaires, the tourist also helps perpetuate another faulty image of modern life — that we never work. It looks as though our technologies do the work for us. In industrial society today, we actually spend more hours working than people in rural, agrarian economies. But that is not how it looks to the Ladakhis. For them, work is physical work, walking, and carrying things. A person sitting behind the wheel of a car or pushing buttons on a typewriter doesn't appear to be working.

One day I had spent ten hours writing letters. I was exhausted, stressed, and had a headache. In the evening, when I complained about being tired because of having worked so hard, the family I was living with laughed; they thought I was joking. In their eyes, I had not been working; I had been sitting in front of a table, nice and clean, no sweat on my brow, pushing a pen across a piece of paper. This was not work. Ladakhis have not yet experienced the sort of stress, boredom, or frustration that is so much a part of our lives in the West. Once, I tried to explain the concept of stress to some villagers. "You mean you get angry because you have to work?" was the response.

Every day I saw people from two cultures, a world apart, looking at each other and seeing superficial, one-dimensional images. Tourists see people carrying loads on their backs and walking long distances over high mountain passes and say, "How terrible; what a life of drudgery." They forget that they have traveled thousands of miles and spent thousands of dollars for the pleasure of walking through the mountains with heavy backpacks. They also forget how much their bodies suffer from lack of use at home. During working hours they get no exercise, so they spend their free time trying to make up for it. Some will even drive to a health club — across a polluted city in rush hour — to sit in a basement, pedaling a bicycle that does not go anywhere. And they actually pay for the privilege.

Development has brought not only tourism, but also Western and Indian films and, more recently, television. Together they provide overwhelming image of luxury and power. There are countless tools and magical gadgets. And there are machines — machines to take pictures, machines to tell the time, machines to make fire, to travel from one place to another, to talk with someone far away. Machines can do everything for you; it is no wonder the tourists look so clean and have such soft hands.

In films, the rich, the beautiful, and the brave lead lives filled with excitement and glamor. For the young Ladakhis, the picture they present is irresistible. By contrast, their own lives seem primitive, silly, and inefficient. The one-dimensional view of modern life becomes a slap in the face. They feel stupid and ashamed. They are asked by their parents to choose a way of life that involves working in the fields and getting their hands dirty for very little or no money. Their own culture seems absurd compared with the world of the tourists and film heroes.

For millions of youths in rural areas of the world, modern Western culture appears far superior to their own. It is not surprising since, looking as they do from the outside, all they can see is the material side of the modern world — the side in which Western culture excels. They cannot so readily see the social or psychological dimensions — the stress, the loneliness, the fear of growing old. Nor can they see environmental decay, inflation, or unemployment. On the other hand, they know their own culture inside out, including all its limitations and perfections.

The sudden influx of Western influence has caused some Ladakhis — the young men in particular — to develop feelings of inferiority. They reject their own culture wholesale, and at the same time eagerly embrace the new one. They rush after the symbols of modernity: sunglasses, Walkmans, and blue jeans several sizes too small — not because they find those jeans more attractive or uncomfortable, but because they are symbols of modern life.

Modern symbols have also contributed to an increase in aggression in Ladakh. Now young boys see violence glamorized on the screen. From Western-style films, they can easily get the impression that if they want to be modern, they should smoke one cigarette after another, get a fast car, and race through the countryside shooting people left and right!

It has been painful to see the changes in young Ladakhi friends. Of course they do not all turn violent, but they do become angry and less secure. I have seen a gentle culture change — a culture in which men, even young men, were happy to cuddle a baby or to be loving and soft with their grandmothers.

Dawa was about fifteen when I met him, and he was still living in his village. When the tourists started coming, he became a guide. He used his donkeys and mules for trekking, as pack animals. I lost contact with him for several years, but I heard that he had started his own tourist agency — one of the first Ladakhis to do so. Then one day in the bazaar I bumped into a young man wearing the latest fashion gear: metallic sunglasses, a T-shirt advertising an American rock band, skin-tight blue jeans, and basketball shoes. It was Dawa.

"I hardly recognized you," I said in Ladakhi.

"Changed a bit, eh?" he replied proudly in English.

We went to a restaurant

crowded with tourists from every part of the globe. Dawa insisted on talking in English.

"You know I'm working for myself now? Business is great, Helena. I have lots of customers and I'm making a lot of money. I have a room in Leh now."

"I'm surprised I haven't seen more of you," I said.

"Well, I'm hardly ever here — I collect the groups myself in Srinagar, and spend most of the time trekking and visiting monasteries."

"You like your new life?"

"I like it. Most of the tourists are real VIPs! Not like these Ladakhis who just laze around all day." He grinned at me. "A surgeon from New York gave me this," he said, pointing to his brand-new backpack.

"Do you go to the village much?"

"Every few months— to take them rice and sugar. And they always want me back to help with the harvest."

"How does it feel to go home?"

"Boring. It's so backward there! We still don't have electricity, and Abi [Grandmother] doesn't want it."

"Maybe she likes the old ways."

"Well, they can be stuck in the old ways if they want, but Ladakh will change around them. We've worked in the fields long enough, Helena; we don't want to work so hard anymore."

"I thought you said Ladakhis just laze around all day."

"I mean they don't know how to get ahead."

Dawa ostentatiously pulled a pack of Marlboros from his pocket. When I turned down his offer, he lit one for himself and leaned toward me with a worried look.

"I had a fight with my girlfriend this morning. I was looking for her when I met you."

"Oh! Who's your girlfriend?"

"I'm not sure I still have a girlfriend, but she's from Holland. She was in one of my tour groups and stayed on to be with me. But she doesn't like it here anymore — she wants to go home. And she wants me to go with her, to live in Holland."

"Would you do that?" I asked.

"I can't leave my family. They need the money I earn. But she can't understand that."

# The Law
# of the
# Market-Place

♦ ♦ ♦

**BY**

**SIBANI**

**RAYCHAUDHURI**

In the back street
of the capital city
stalls and shops stretch out
on to the pavement.
Passers-by stop to examine
crates, baskets, sacks
and jars
filled with colour and abundance.

Fragrant rice
and freshwater fish
from Bangladesh,
cloves and cinnamon sticks
from Tangiers,
marrows and chilies
from East Africa stimulate
the palates of the rich and the exiled.

Surprise and curiosity for some —
nostalgia for others
who've left behind
a piece of land
where golden hopes were planted.

They till the land
and harvest the crops
but don't taste them.
They pack them, load them on to
ships to the West.
Arms, ammunition, come back in return.

# Holy Cow

♦ ♦ ♦

BY

SEHDEV

KUMAR

All across the world, on many a street corner, the proud words are there for everyone to see: "85 billion served." Over the years, in my neighbourhood, I have watched this number go up in such quick strides that any attempt at equating it with the growth in world population has eluded me. Not long ago, every man, woman and child in the world could have been served 10 McDonald's hamburgers. Now, with the world population at 5.5 billion, the ratio of Macs consumed and the human consumers has moved to 15 for each, and it is increasing every day.

Yet curiously, at the Earth Summit in Rio de Janeiro, there are many who are deeply concerned about the exploding world population — particularly in the developing countries — but are unaware of the astronomical explosion of Macs, and their busy meaty progeny.

The two, however, are very much connected, even if expanding population is regarded a sign of underdevelopment and meat consumption a sign of progress.

Since 1950, the human population has doubled. Global meat production has nearly quadrupled, and domestic animals now outnumber humans by three to one.

"An alien ecologist observing...Earth might conclude," wrote a biologist, "that cattle is the dominant animal species."

The cattle and other cud-chewing livestock graze half the planet's land area. Along with pigs and poultry, they also eat feed and fodder raised on one-quarter of the cropland.

The impact of livestock on the global environment — water systems, energy consumption, soils and forests, and human health and economy — is colossal.

For thousands of years, domesticated animals have played a prominent, beneficial role in the welfare of humans, providing food, fuel, transport, fertilizer and clothing. But in this century, the numbers and impact of livestock have swelled apace with human population and affluence.

For industrial cultures and

for urban people everywhere, animals are just food. But cattle were originally domesticated as beasts of burden. Even today, throughout Africa and Asia, 89 to 90 per cent of agricultural land is plowed by draft animals.

Their manure is also a precious fertilizer and fuel in developing countries. In India, for instance, it supplies about 30 per cent of the fuel for the rural population of some 650 million people.

For hundreds of years, and in some areas even today, crop production and livestock rearing went hand in hand, keeping farms ecologically balanced. Modern agricultural practices in the livestock industry have changed all that, radically.

As more and more livestock is fed on energy-rich grain and protein-rich soybean meals, increasingly larger areas of the world's cropland produce grain for animals. As much as 38 per cent of the world's grain is fed to livestock. In the United States, the figure is 70 per cent. Worldwide, the area planted with soybeans for animals has increased fourfold since 1950.

All these changes have had crucial impact on the lives of the poor, and, in turn, on population growth.

In Mexico, the share of land used for growing animal feed and fodder increased almost fivefold in the 20 years from 1960 to 1980. Consequently, all staple foods for the poor — corn, rice, wheat and beans — are being grown on a steadily decreasing land area. Although 22 per cent of Mexicans suffer from malnutrition, Mexico feeds 30 per cent of its grain to livestock.

The study of data from one country after another — Egypt, Brazil, Colombia, Mexico, Peru, the Philippines, Thailand, South Africa — reveals that the demand for meat by the rich has been squeezing out production of staples for the poor.

By the late 1970s, these new developments had turned a great many Third World countries from exporters of grain into importers. The change was due only partly to growing populations — more than 75 per cent of the imports of corn, barley, sorghum and oats were used for meat production, often for export.

The result is that more and more wealth — as much as $50 billion in a decade — continues to move from Third World to industrial countries. For instance, half Central America's agricultural land produces food for export, while in several of its countries the poorest 50 per cent of the population eats only half the necessary protein.

Yet governments everywhere

— in Costa Rica, Brazil, Botswana, Sudan — and international agencies too, coddle the livestock producers and give billions in subsidies, tax credits and technical assistance.

In 1990, according to the Organization for Economic Co-operation and Development, government programs in its member states provided subsidies to animal farmers and feed growers worth $120 billion. Almost 20 per cent of the Soviet national budget went to food subsidies in 1990, much of this for animal products.

Nightmarish scenarios will be created at the Earth Summit about the explosion of the "population bomb." But many holy cows will be left unhindered.

# Village
# People

♦ ♦ ♦

**BY**

**BESSIE**

**HEAD**

**P**overty has a home in Africa — like a quiet second skin. It may be the only place on earth where it is worn with an unconscious dignity. People do not look down at your shoes which are caked with years of mud and split so that the toes stick out. They look straight and deeply into your eyes to see if they are friend or foe. That is all that matters. To some extent I think that this eye-looking, this intense human awareness, is a reflection of the earth all about. There is no end to African sky and African land. One might say that in its vastness is a certain kind of watchfulness that strips humans down to their simplest forms. If that is not so, then there must be some other, unfathomable reason for the immense humanity and the extreme gentleness of the people of my village.

Poverty here has major backing. Our lives are completely adapted to it. Each day we eat a porridge of millet in the morning; a thicker millet porridge with a piece of boiled meat at midday; and at evening we repeat breakfast. We use our heads to transport almost everything: water from miles and miles, bags of corn and maize, and fire wood.

This adaptation to difficult conditions in a permanently drought-stricken country is full of calamity. Babies die most easily of starvation and malnutrition: and yet, within this pattern of adaptation people crowd in about the mother and sit, in heavy silence, absorbing the pain, till, to the mother, it is only a dim, dull ache folded into the stream of life. It is not right. There is a terrible mindlessness about it. But what alternative? To step out of this mindless safety, and face the pain of life alone when the balance is heavily weighted down on one side, is for certain to face a fate far worse. Those few who have, are insane in a strange, quiet, harmless way: walking all about the village, freely. Only by their ceaseless muttering and half-clothed bodies are they distinguishable from others. It is not right, as it is negative merely to strive for existence. There must be other ingredients boiling in the pot. Yet how? We are in the middle of nowhere. Most communication is by ox-cart or sledge. Poverty also creates strong currents of fear and anxiety. We are not outgoing. We tend to push aside all new intrusions. We live and survive by making as few demands as possible. Yet, under the deceptive peace around us we are more easily confused and torn apart than those with the capacity to take in their stride the width and the reach of new horizons.

Do we really retain the right to develop slowly, admitting change only in so far as it keeps pace with our limitations, or does change descend upon us as a calamity? I merely ask this because, anonymous as we are, in our favour is a great credit balance of love and warmth that the Gods somewhere should count up. It may be that they overlook desert and semi-desert places. I should like to remind them that there are people here too who need taking care of.

## The Old Woman

She was so frail that her whole body swayed this way and that like a thin stalk of corn in the wind. Her arms were as flat as boards. The flesh hung loosely, and her hands which clutched the walking stick were turned outwards and knobbled with age. Under her long dress also swayed the tattered edges of several petticoats. The ends of two bony stick-legs peeped out. She had on a pair of sand-shoes. The toes were all sticking out, so that the feet flapped about in them. She wore each shoe on the wrong foot, so that it made the heart turn over with amusement.

Yet she seemed so strong that it was a shock when she suddenly bent double, retched and coughed emptily, and crumbled to the ground like a quiet sigh.

"What is it, mmm? What is the matter?" I asked.

"Water, water," she said faintly.

"Wait a minute. I shall ask at this hut here if there is any water."

"What is the matter?" they asked.

"The old lady is ill," I said.

"No," she said curtly. "I am not ill. I am hungry."

The crowd laughed in embarrassment that she should display her need so nakedly. They turned away, but old ladies have no more shame left. They are like children. They give way to weakness and cry openly when they are hungry.

"Never mind," I said. Hunger is a terrible thing. My hut is not far away. This small child will take you. Wait till I come back, then I shall prepare food for you."

Then, it was late afternoon. The old lady had long ago passed from my mind when a strange young woman, unknown to me, walked into the yard with a pail of water on her head. She set it down outside the door and squatted low.

"Good-day. How are you?" I said.

She returned the greeting, keeping her face empty and carefully averted. It is impossible to say: what do you want? Whom are you looking for? It is impossible to say this to a carefully averted face and a body that squats quietly, patiently. I looked at the sky, helplessly. I looked at the trees. I looked at the ground, but the young woman said nothing. I did not know her, inside or out. Many people I do not know who know me, inside and out, and always it is this way, this silence.

A curious neighbour looked over the hedge.

"What's the matter?" she asked.

I turned my eyes to the sky again, shrugging helplessly.

"Please ask the young woman what she wants, whom she is looking for."

The young woman turned her face to the neighbour, still keeping it averted, and said quietly:

"No, tell her she helped our relative who collapsed this morning. Tell her the relatives discussed the matter. Tell her we had nothing to give in return, only that one relative said she passes by every day on her way to the water tap. Then we decided to give a pail of water. It is all we have."

Tell them too. Tell them how natural, sensible, normal is human kindness. Tell them, those who judge my country, Africa, by gain and greed, that the gods walk about her barefoot with no ermine and gold-studded cloaks.

## Summer Sun

All day long I lie asleep under the thorn tree, and the desert is on this side of me and on that side of me. I have no work to do. We are all waiting for the rain, as we cannot plough without rain. I think the rain has gone away again, like last year. We had a little rain in November, but December has gone, and now it is January, and each day we have been sitting here, waiting for rain: my mother, my grandmother and my grandfather, my cousin Lebenah, and my sister and her little baby. If it were to rain my grandfather would push the plough and my cousin Lebenah would pull the oxen across the great miles of our land. We women would follow behind, sowing maize, millet, pumpkin and watermelon seed. I feel great pity for my family, and other families. I wonder why we sit here like this. Each day the sun is hot, hot in the blue sky. Each day the water pool of November rain gets smaller. Soon we will have to leave the land and return to the village.

In the village we have a politician who takes the people up on the hill to pray for rain. He wears a smart suit and has a big black car and a beautiful deep African voice. His mind is quick and moves from one thing to another. He can pray, and cry, and speak politics all at once. People always expect the rain to fall the minute after he has stopped praying and crying. They call him the one who has shaken God loose.

Actually, I have not been sleeping the whole day. I am trying to learn English. My cousin Lebenah tells me that things are changing in Africa, and that it is necessary for women to improve themselves. I love my cousin Lebenah so much that I do anything he tells me to do. He tells me that English is the best language to learn, as many books have been written in English, and that there is no end to the knowledge that can be gained from them. He gave me a geography book and I have read it over and over. I am puzzled and afraid. Each year the sun is more cruel. Each year the rain becomes less and less. Each year more and more of our cattle die. The only animal that survives is the goat. It can eat anything and we eat the goat. Without the goat, I do not know what we would do. It is all about us, like the family. It has the strangest eyes. They are big and yellow, and the pupil is a black streak right across the yellow ball of the eye.

I am trying to improve myself too, as I am very afraid that I may have an illegitimate baby like my elder sister. My family will suffer much. And the child too. It may die. There is never enough food and we are always hungry. It is not so easy for a woman to have too many babies. She has to think about how she will feed the baby, clothe it, and wash it. My sister's baby is lovely, though. He laughs a lot for no reason at all.

My geography book makes me wonder and wonder. It tells me that water is formed by hydrogen and oxygen. I wonder so much about that. If we had green things everywhere, they might help to make the oxygen to make the rain. The soil is very fertile. If there is only a little rain, green things come out everywhere, and many strange flowers. How can we live like this? Here are our bags with the seeds of maize, and millet, and the land is hard as stone.

Tomorrow the sun will rise, quietly. The many birds in the bush will welcome it. I do not. Alone, without the help of rain it is cruel, killing and killing. All day we look on it, like on death. Then, at evening, all is as gentle as we are. Mother roasts goat meat over the coals of the wood fire. Sister feeds her baby. Grandfather and cousin Lebenah talk quietly to each other about little things. The stars spread across the sky and bend down at the horizon. The quiet talk of grandfather and cousin Lebenah seem to make earth and heaven come together. I do not know what we would do if we all did not love one another, because tomorrow the sun will rise again.

# Hunger

**♦ ♦ ♦**

**BY**

**LAURENCE**

**BINYON**

I come among the peoples like a shadow.
I sit down by each man's side.

None sees me, but they look on one another,
And know that I am there.

My silence is like the silence of the tide
That buries the playground of children;

Like the deepening of frost in the slow night,
When birds are dead in the morning.

Armies trample, invade, destroy,
With guns roaring from earth and air.

Kings and chancellors give commands,
I give no command to any;

But I am listened to more than kings
And more than passionate orators.

I unswear words, and undo deeds.
Naked things know me.

I am the first and last to be felt of the living.
I am Hunger.

# The Unofficial Ambassadors

◆ ◆ ◆

BY

DEBRA

BLACK

**W**hen Doreen McConachie, a public health nurse working for CUSO in Lima, Peru, heard the news of yet another assassination by the Shining Path, a Maoist terrorist group, she was devastated.

This time the terrorists had brutally murdered Maria Elena Moyano, the deputy mayor of the nearby shantytown Villa El Salvador.

The terrorists shot and killed Moyano and then blew up her corpse with two kilograms of dynamite.

McConachie respected Moyano and had met her three times, most recently when the Peruvian community leader had spoken at a regional meeting of CUSO in November, 1991.

She and thousands of others filled the shantytown's square as priests offered a mass in memory of Moyano.

"It makes our problems in Canada seem very unreal, very insignificant when you compare them to the problems that happen here in Peru," McConachie says in an interview from CUSO offices in Lima.

She is one of thousands of Canadians who test their principles of altruism and caring daily, working in Third World hot spots and developing countries such as Peru, Bolivia, Sudan, Kenya, the Philippines and even former communist strongholds like Hungary and Czechoslovakia.

Canadians like Mauro Tartaglia, Sheila Wilson, Beat Rohr and others often put their own personal comfort and safety aside in an attempt to help the world's desperate and dispossessed, working through international and national relief agencies such as CUSO, CIDA (Canadian International Development Agency), the Red Cross, United Nations, CARE Canada, and the Canadian Executive Services Organization to name but a few.

They are unofficial ambassadors who let the world know Canada cares.

McConachie, 38, first arrived

in Peru in 1988 to work as a nurse and midwife in the northern Andes.

She had always wanted to work in a Third World country and decided when she was 35 that it was time to pack her bags and leave her job as a rural nurse in Gibson, B.C., before she got too settled.

She was well prepared for the rigors of the job. Her training as a midwife in England and her studies at the University of Victoria for a nursing degree came in handy as she faced the women and children in the remote mountain villages.

The two years she spent in the mountains were rough, but rewarding, particularly when she set up a course in traditional midwifery for women in several remote villages.

Then, in 1990, she moved from the rural highlands to Lima where she set up shop at the CUSO offices doing recruitment, orientation and follow-up on health care programs.

Life in Peru is anything but boring, she says. The troubled political and economic scene is taking its toll on thousands of Peruvians, particularly women, children and labor groups.

Shantytowns surround Lima and millions of Peruvians live in dire poverty without enough water and food. "The people are so poor here, you can't imagine."

Even those who work can't necessarily afford to eat. For example, the minimum salary in Peru is $78 a month but a food basket for a family of four, including food and transportation, runs about $350 a month. "That gives you a sense of the poverty here."

Since her stint in Peru, McConachie has become a firm believer in the ideals of social justice and change. "Before I came to Peru I had not been involved in any related work. I had done a little bit of work in the peace movement but nothing very militant. But coming here...you couldn't be here and work in Peru without becoming involved.

"The situation in developing countries isn't going to change until there are changes in attitudes in countries like Canada. We have to change our attitudes about consumerism and a kind of egocentrism. The majority of the world's resources come from developing countries but the majority is used by developed countries."

◆ ◆ ◆

The poverty and political uncertainty of life in Peru has also affected Mauro Tartaglia, a 39-year-old relief worker who works with CARE supervising projects designed to stimulate jobs and establish a small business sector.

Tartaglia, originally from Italy, makes his home in Canada with his wife and three children when he's not out in the field. But he's been out working in the field for more than a decade.

A civil engineer, he first began working with a group of United Nations volunteers in 1977 in the Ivory Coast, building markets and houses. Since then he's worked and travelled to such far-flung places as Nicaragua and Indonesia.

But no matter where he goes, one sentiment follows him: "I have a personal belief in the unity of the world. I wanted to help other people, to do something useful.

"We feel like we have a special opportunity to be useful," explains Tartaglia, shouting over the crackle of long-distance telephone wires from his office in Peru's capital.

"Lima has 7 million people. The large cities have attracted literally millions of people who are trying to improve their living conditions. It doesn't always happen. This means millions of people are living in slums and we try to help these people."

So Tartaglia and his team run a number of projects in these slums outside Lima, including programs to give young people a trade such as carpentry or shoe-making.

Even something as simple as taking a shower can't be taken for granted, Tartaglia says.

Peru is now suffering from the ravages of a drought and heat wave, he says. So he and his wife are teaching their children how to save water and not waste it, since it is such a precious resource.

◆ ◆ ◆

Sheila Wilson, who makes her home in Newfoundland, is another Canadian who has seen action in relief circles around the world.

A nurse with the International Federation of Red Cross, Wilson was first inspired to work in the Third World when she heard a 1979 appeal by the Red Cross asking for help at a refugee camp on the Cambodia-Thailand border.

She decided to leave her job at the Canadian Red Cross in Newfoundland and heed the call to medical arms.

"It was the first time I saw people with absolutely nothing," the 39-year-old says in a telephone interview from her office in Khartoum, Sudan.

"We did a lot of emergency medicine because of the shelling. It was a real shock for me to see people living in such abject conditions. The contrast is so great between that and life in Canada."

From the conflict on the Cambodia-Thailand border she went to Ethiopia to work on a famine relief project in the mid-1980s.

She firmly believes in the Red Cross and the work she does.

"If people are in need, we are able to reach them. No one gets preferential treatment. The symbol of the Red Cross is well-known around the world and is respected. It allows you much broader scope in your work. I believe in what the Red Cross is trying to do for people."

Wilson is now a medical co-ordinator with the Red Cross, supervising health care programs, food distribution and medical care for the 1 million displaced people living on the outskirts of Khartoum. She also supervises an emergency feeding program at a refugee camp for Ethiopian and Eritrean refugees in Sudan.

Wilson and her husband, who also works in Sudan with an American refugee program, both find their work deeply satisfying.

But she acknowledges it can be depressing.

"It's difficult sometimes to keep a perspective on it. There are certain times when it hits you..." she says as her voice trails off. A long pause follows — a pause that seems even more poignant over the thousands of kilometres that separate her from home.

Still, Wilson gets a tremendous gratification from her work. She can see results quickly, whether she's distributing food, providing emergency medicine or giving vaccinations.

Social responsibility is what drew Beat Rohr, a native of Switzerland who now calls Canada his home, to life in relief work.

As country director for CARE in Nairobi, Kenya, he and his staff provide relief for three refugee camps near the Somalian and Ethiopian borders.

The one-time Quebec farmer is devoted to helping those less fortunate. He's spent time working in Ethiopia, Sudan and Nicaragua.

"I've always had an interest in development issues in the Third World," he says. "As a child I was interested in working at some level for social justice and this is one way to do it."

As Rohr explains what has drawn him to this life, his 5-year-old daughter calls out to him, her tiny voice barely audible over the phone lines. She wants him to come and tuck her into bed and read a story.

Like any father and daughter, she and Rohr share quiet family moments that ease the despair so pervasive in the refugee camps.

"One of the frustrating things about this work is emergencies keep happening, over and over again. There is so much civil strife, drought situations. It is very frustrating. There doesn't seem to be an end to it."

But that's why Rohr and others try to emphasize economic issues, so they can give the population a means to sustain themselves.

"As you know, the situation in Somalia is extremely bad. The country's in civil war. People who are displaced are women and children. They need a safety net and that's what we're trying to provide."

◆ ◆ ◆

But it's not just war or famine relief that sends Canadians all over the globe.

Some like Stan MacLellan, an investment counsellor, Howard Walker, a retired architect, and Sheila Russek, a specialist in cable manufacturing, volunteer their time and expertise to help business or government.

Through the Canadian Executive Services Organization, a non-profit volunteer group, these three have done more than just talk about social action.

In 1992 MacLellan, a partner in Cockfield, Porretti, Cunningham Investment Counsel, found himself working in both Czechoslovakia and Hungary, advising government officials on everything from agricultural policy to investment funds and venture capital for housing.

Meanwhile, his wife was also volunteering in both countries, teaching English and working with an environmental group.

While MacLellan was offering economic advice, the 54-year-old also learned a thing or two from his former communist employers.

"They could probably teach us something about social values. They're very socially conscious and aware of the needs of others," he says from his hotel in Budapest.

"One thing that is very obvious to me is we're all one family," adds Walker, in his early 60s, from his base in Tarija, Bolivia, where he is working on restoring and adapting a 16th century grain mill.

"Whatever each one of us can do to make a more harmonious family is important. I know that sounds ridiculously idealistic but that's how I feel."

That's how his wife feels as well.

She, too, is volunteering

through CESO, working on the interior design of a hotel.

"When you look at the rest of the world, we're so fortunate in Canada. I just feel it's an opportunity to give something back."

That sentiment is what moved Russek, 56, and her husband Roman, 69, to go to the Philippines.

Both are highly trained in the cable industry and felt it would be a shame to waste their years of expertise after they retired.

So instead of staying home in Scarborough, they decided, like so many other Canadian volunteers abroad, to give their life some additional meaning.

"Roman and I feel when one is living a life entirely for yourself and even your own family, it eventually becomes hollow. You have to be somewhere doing something for other people, otherwise your life loses its meaning."

# The Third World

◆ ◆ ◆

**BY**

**IAN**

**KEELING**

*A group of volunteer young men and women travel to Africa to help build school houses for a poor village.*

*A celebrity stands on late night TV and asks for a donation so that a starving child might eat.*

Often when we think of the term "Third World development" these are two of the more frequent images to appear in our minds. And while these two images may not be completely wrong, they paint a very narrow picture of the Third World. What they don't show us is that the situation in the Third World is hopeful. A great deal of work is being done, not only by North Americans, but also by the very people who have to endure those problems. Another thing those images fail to convey is that combating these problems can be more than volunteering; it can be a full-time occupation.

International development as a career requires many skills and talents. Overseas work in emergency relief, community development, or education are important fields of international development. For every lesson we teach we learn one in return.

So what do you need for such a career? Start with an interest in people, because that's what the job is all about. It's not about how many tonnes of food were sent to Ethiopia in 1991 or how many schools were built in Costa Rica. It's about people. A willingness to make sacrifices. Odd hours and hard work. Getting rich it's not. Patience and the ability to listen it is. People in developing countries understand their problems and often have their own viable solutions. What they want and need is co-operative assistance. It's all about working together.

Get as much volunteer experience as you can for this shows the organizations your willingness to sacrifice. Working in a day care centre or hospital is good experience. Of course overseas experience is essential. There are several national organizations that are specifically oriented towards giving young people overseas experience and many have regional offices. Volunteering for these organizations is an important first step if you're looking for a career. They open eyes to a world never seen before.

## This is not charity

Kevin Perkins was 17, travelling in Greece, and launched a conversation that changed his life. After returning to Canada he began to explore the possibilities of working in overseas development.

After an exchange to India through Canada World Youth, a degree in International Development at the University of Toronto, several other overseas exchanges and a lot of hard work, Kevin, now 28, has a full-time job at Canadian Physicians for Aid and Relief (CPAR).

As program officer for CPAR, an organization which focusses on fighting hunger in the horn of Africa through relief and community development, Kevin is responsible for initiating new programs. This involves writing proposals for a new program, registering as an NGO (Non Governmental Organization) in

the country where the program will take place, and approaching donors here in Canada to help finance the program.

Because the actual implementation of most of the programs is done by local organizations in Africa, once a program is in place, Kevin's job turns to administrative support. This involves visiting the project, writing a report, offering whatever ideas he may have and finding out what other needs the local organizations have. Kevin says, "I don't go over there and dictate. I'm just making suggestions, getting feedback, and finding out what I should be doing here to make their job easier."

Indeed, many people in Canada don't realize that most of the work in overseas development is done by the local people who usually know the solution to their problem and merely require assistance from groups like CPAR. "A lot of people think of Ethiopia as a burnt out desert and Ethiopians as hopeless, powerless people. We pity them but we don't respect them as human beings who are resourceful and ingenious in their survival mechanisms [and] their ability to survive against such impossible odds and keep a smile on their face."

Kevin's advice to anyone interested in a career in international development is find a way to get practical work experience, such as an exchange, because many aspects of the job can't be learned in the classroom. Also, plan to work hard. "It's not an easy thing to do. You have to plan ahead. It takes a lot of letters, a lot of contacts, a lot of making it happen. Not just with people in Canada, but making direct contact with people overseas."

Some might think such a career would leave no time for a family life; however, Kevin is happily married to his wife Donna. "It is difficult," Kevin says. "You have to make compromises, but I think you have to do that in any career. Most people I know whose families live with them in Africa or Asia speak of those years as the best years."

**Optimism is essential**

It is very rare for someone to know what they want to do in life and then find it. However, that's exactly what Tonia de Sousa-Shields has done. She says, "I always wanted to work for an international development organization that is based in Latin America with children and education projects." And as the outreach co-ordinator for Pueblito, a Toronto-based organization that focusses on Latin America, she has found her place in life.

Because Pueblito has three staff in the office, "everybody does a lot of everything." However, Tonia's primary area of focus is Canadian programs — developing education, fundraising, promotion, working with volunteers and committees here in

Canada. As Tonia says, "A lot of international development happens here." She also has special projects to handle, such as organizing funding for an electronic communications network to improve relationships with partner organizations overseas. And as working with children is of great interest to her, she is also helping to organize an early childhood education workshop where several countries will come together to discuss childhood education here in Canada and abroad.

The interest in development overseas started in high school for Tonia, who is now 25. Membership in a United Nations Club was Tonia's first step to her career. She did a student exchange through the Rotary Club to Brazil for 9 months, then took a degree in Latin American studies, giving her academic and practical work experience that organizations look for.

Tonia found out about Pueblito by flipping through a booklet at a university careers centre. At first she had to take a waitressing job to supplement the money she made as a trainee, but eventually she was given a full-time position and her career was set.

Two to three weeks each year Tonia travels to Latin America to keep in touch with the community groups Pueblito is working with. Such trips can often involve experiences ranging from the bizarre (sharing an elevator with a Brazilian 'death squad' leader) to the heart-warming (watching a group of street children write the mayor of their town for a new soccer ball). "Meeting so many wonderful people, hearing so many stories," is the job perk she treasures most.

These people, these stories, help Tonia sustain her optimism, which is perhaps the most important trait one can have in international development. She says, "You can see that things are changing and that little changes are going to make a big difference."

From June '91 of *TG Magazine...Voices of Today's Generation*

# Zack's
# Notebook

◆ ◆ ◆

**BY**

**SARAH**

**PIRTLE**

*It's July in Larkspur, Massachusetts, and 13-year-old Cassie has become friends with Zack who's 16 and a newcomer to the town. They find that they share many interests, especially drawing and art. Zack has just invited Cassie to his house to show her something he's been working on.*

I couldn't wait. I biked all the way up the hill without even walking my bike. The bet I made with myself was that Zack and I would keep having fun together, and he wouldn't forget about me as soon as school started.

When we arrived, we went inside to say hello to his mother who was typing in her study. Then Zack grabbed a pitcher of iced mint tea out of the refrigerator and poured it over ice cubes into two tall glasses. I carried them outside while he went to get whatever it was he wanted to show me.

My favorite place in their yard is a grassy spot in the back that's surrounded by huge snowball bushes. I put the tea down and lay on the grass to wait. I could smell honeysuckle in the air. I thought back to all that Zack had said to me this morning, like about having twin imaginations, and wondered what his surprise would be.

He returned with a faded blue three-ring notebook that was so worn many of the threads were coming apart from the blue cover.

"Are these drawings?" I asked.

"Well, you'll see. A little of everything. I don't really draw. I collect."

I read the cover. In block lettering he had written "EXPERIMENTS IN PEACE." It looked like it could have said "EXPERIMENTS IN CHEMISTRY." I liked the fact that it wasn't decorated with a lot of peace signs. It was plain, and that made it look more serious.

He put the notebook in my hands and let me open it. The first page inside had a dot in the center surrounded by seven circles, each larger than the next. That was all. I looked up at Zack for an explanation, but the expression on his face seemed to say, "You'll figure it out. Keep going." He looked pleased to be showing the notebook to me, as if I were unwrapping a present or figuring out a puzzle he had designed.

Beyond that page, there were section dividers. The first divider was labeled on the side, "The World." I skipped that for a moment and read the next: "America and Other Countries." I opened it up.

There was a photo of a building that had to be the White House. Two girls were standing in front of it reading letters. "That's Hannah and Nessa Rubin," said Zack as if he was particularly glad I'd started there. "They're from Vermont, and they brought thousands of letters to the President. Can you imagine it, Cassie? They collected that many letters."

"Who from?" I asked.

"Kids. All over the country. I wrote them a letter, too. I was in junior high."

"About what? What do the letters say?"

"The kinds of things that your pictures say."

I felt tiny bubbles of excitement. Here were kids who would like my drawings, who would understand what they were about.

"Where are they now?"

"You mean, Hannah and Nessa? In college, I guess, or maybe graduated. A friend of a friend gave me the photo. He was there at the White House, too. About a dozen kids were with them."

" And they read all the letters out loud?"

"Yup, they read them all. They were supposed to meet with a press secretary and give their letters to him, but he canceled their meeting. And the mail room wouldn't accept their delivery, so they refused to leave."

I couldn't imagine even writing the President's press secretary, let alone standing in front of the White House fence. I liked knowing there were kids like that somewhere.

I turned the page and found another photo. "What's this group doing?" I asked Zack.

"They're from S.T.O.P. Do you know what it is?"

"Yeah."

I'd heard of S.T.O.P. groups before from my mother. The first group began near here at the Northfield Mount Hermon School about the same time she was going to a lot of movies and talks about peace work. I knew that the letters stood for Student/Teacher Organization To Prevent Nuclear War.

"Well, those kids are planting a rose bush in their school court-yard. It's like a wish for peace, Cass. You know what I mean?"

I did. I thought about my drawing of flowers from the meadow. That morning each of them had seemed like a wish for peace.

"Where did you get the photo?" I asked.

"My social studies teacher. Four of us did a project on kids who are peacemakers. The whole thing is in there." He looked at it with me.

I saw a newspaper article about a children's art exchange with kids in the Soviet Union, a flyer about a camp called the International Children's Summer Village, lots of drawings, and a couple of short reports.

I'd never heard of these kids before, except for Samantha Smith. I'd seen her picture in the newspaper when she went to the Soviet Union. These were regular kids — and there were so many of them! Each group was doing something different.

I saw a photo of teenagers at the Northfield Mount Hermon School acting out a play they'd written about their secret fears of nuclear war. It was called, "Changing the Silence." And there was a flyer about Jody Lester and Maya Gillingham who went on a tour to different high schools in 1984 to get others talking about their own hopes and fears. They sounded brave. Of course they'd never come to Frontier High in Larkspur. Our principal would never have let them in.

"Who drew this picture?"

"Carlos. That's a S.T.O.P. group getting on a boat in Japan. If we couldn't find a photo, we would make up what it probably looked like. I shouldn't say 'we,' Cass. I just wrote things and helped with the thinking. The others were the real artists. You'll see when you find the charts I drew." He made a face. "Except you could say," he added, "that this whole notebook is my drawing. I draw with my mind."

I don't like to hear people say they can't draw because I think everybody can, but I didn't know what to say about it then, so I just kept going. I turned the page. "Did Carlos draw this?"

"No, Cheryl did that as a going-away present. That's Carlos on the left, with Tony and Cheryl. I already miss them a lot. Well, that's the end of that section." He went inside to get some paper.

I read all the headings on the dividers now. They were, in order: "The World"; "America and Other Countries"; "Inside America"; "Our State"; "Our City" (which had been crossed out and now read, "Our Town," I guess for Larkspur) "Other People"; "My Family and Me." The last one was marked private so I didn't read that, but I crisscrossed through most of the others. Seven headings. That explained the seven circles in the front.

It was like a scrapbook. He had stapled in clippings from newspapers and magazines and photocopies of articles. He had lists of books to read, and he'd checked off the ones he had finished. He had photos from magazines and photos he'd taken and a few more drawings by his old friends. Lots of the sections seemed to have ideas he'd thought up himself. There were charts and sketches for streets and buildings and machines. I knew Zack must have done them himself because the squiggle of the lines looked exactly like his handwriting. "You are an artist, Zack," I thought to myself.

I wanted to go back and see how his mind would draw the world so I turned to that first section. I could tell by the funny block shaped lettering that Zack had typed the words on a computer.

## WORLD COMPUTER BANK

It's 2012. The computer experts from every country have teamed up for peace. They work for the new world government now. Computer One holds a list of every country, how many people live there, how much food they need to get from other countries, and what kind of food they can grow themselves. It helps make sure that the food in the world goes to people who need it, so no one needs to starve anymore.

Computer Two houses information abut the radioactive materials in the world and where they are stored. There's a phone hook-up to talk to the guards and some way to alert the computer if a leak starts in any of the storage places.

Computer Three does the same with poisons and chemical wastes. There's also a way to check up on any clean-up program going on in any place in the world. BLEEP!

"Hello, India? How's your work going cleaning up the Ganges River?"

Computer Four monitors all nuclear weapons sites. It helps to verify that all peace treaties are working.

I paused. I liked reading about these things. Just seeing them on paper helped them begin to come true in my mind.

I glanced ahead in the section. Zack had made up fifteen different ideas for what computers could do to help the world government. Some were typed, some handwritten, some so scrawled I could hardly understand them.

"I keep working on the list, adding more when I get a new thought," Zack told me. A funny image popped into my head of Zack suddenly getting an inspiration while he's swimming out to the raft in Larkspur Lake. He's half way there, but he spins around and swims back to land, dries off his hands with a beach towel, and makes a new entry before he can lose his thought. Or he's playing outfield in a baseball game. An idea comes to him, and while the catcher is fumbling with a stray ball, he takes out a pen and writes it on his blue jeans. Up, sounds like Zack.

I turned to the section called "Other People." This had lists like "Why People Fight With Each Other," "Experiments in Breaking Up Fights," (with dates and descriptions of what he tried to do and whether it worked), "Why I Get Mad at People," and "What is an Enemy?" I spent a lot of time looking at that.

Then there was a list called "Peacemakers." There were names of people I recognized right away, like Martin Luther King, and others I'd never heard of before. There was a page for each letter of the alphabet. For instance, under F it had Randy Forsberg.

"Who's Randy Forsberg?" I asked him. I was embarrassed not to know.

"She's the person who first thought of the Nuclear Weapons Freeze. We studied her in school."

"And who's this next person, Lionel Franklin?"

"Oh, Lionel. Great guy. He lived on our block in Syracuse. He gave out winter clothes to anybody who needed them. He kept a whole room of gloves and scarves and jackets and boots. People would give Lionel their old clothes." He sounded like a peacemaker all right, although it seemed unusual to put him right next to Randy Forsberg. Still, it made sense when I thought about it more.

I wanted to see what other ideas he had come up with. I turned to a new essay:

## The High School I Wish I Went To

No more walking from class to class in a cinder block building that's just a cut above a jail. No more being judged by how you do on a multiple choice test instead of how you think and write and solve problems. No more sitting in rows. No more wondering how you're going to get through the next boring minutes, hours, weeks, months.

What would make it better? For one thing — Projects! Projects that you sign up for yourself, that could take you out of the building to work with anybody who can teach what you want to know.

I guess you couldn't do expensive projects like flying to India or living in China for a year. But if I had my way, I'd work on the *Clearwater.*

"What's the *Clearwater?*" I hesitated asking. Maybe everybody knew but me.

"It's a boat that sails up and down the Hudson River. It teaches people about water pollution, and it's helped get people to clean it up so now you can swim in it again. I've heard the river used to be as muddy as coffee, and now you can see clear to the bottom."

"Wow. That's a big change."

"My parents and I drive down there every summer for the *Clearwater's* Hudson River Revival. It's a folk music festival, and it's so great, Cass. Thousands of people come to it now. I used to wish I could sneak on board the ship and just run away and never come home."

In Zack's description of the way he wanted things to be, every city and town that had a lake or river near it would have a small boat like the *Clearwater.* For science class, kids would help scientists test water samples to see how clean the water was each week. Then for English class, they'd put the results into an article for the town newspaper to print. In art class, you could make a comic strip for kids about pollution. For social studies class, you'd track down anybody who was polluting the water and go talk to them.

I'd love to go to a school like that. I'd want to do different projects, of course, than the ones he'd thought of. If I could get credit by working with a different artist in Larkspur every year, I'd stop dreading waking up Monday mornings. I thought of myself going off to school and not getting on the school bus. Instead, I'd walk around the corner to the potter's house. I'd be in heaven.

I turned the page, and Zack leaned over my shoulder to see where I was. The next section had a lot of cross-outs and things stapled and pasted on. "I'll just explain this next part." We were in the "Our State" section. "For starters, every single town in the state would have its own recycling center and its own safe energy department."

This section didn't sound as interesting to me. "Larkspur already has a recycling center," I said trying to hurry it along.

"Yeah, well, Larkspur is ahead of lots of the others. But I know it doesn't have a conflict resolution center."

"What would that do?"

"If people were having a fight, like if two neighbors were arguing about the dog that one of them owned or about anything and they couldn't work it out, they would go and get help settling it."

"They should call it the fight center."

"But it would do other things, too. Like if parents were getting a divorce and they were trying to figure out what was best for the kids, they would get help there. Or if teachers wanted to teach their class how to get along and settle problems better, someone from the conflict resolution center would come and help at the school."

"We could have used that last year in our class," I said. "By the end of the year, there were two big cliques and the kids hated each other. There were fights on the playground and lots of yelling in class. Miss Fielding, our teacher, looked happier when school let out than I did."

"You hungry yet?"

"Yeah." I hadn't packed any lunch before I'd hurried out that morning.

"I'll go in and make something. Do you like meat loaf sandwiches?"

"With lots of ketchup." When he went inside, I turned back to an earlier section and read some more. I found a clipping from a magazine about a solar-powered city in Arizona called Arcosanti that would house five thousand people when it was finished. Right after that there was another clipping from a 1981 copy of *Soviet Life* about a solar-powered city in an area called Ashkabad.

I put the notebook down and lay back on the grass. I heard the loud buzz of a queen bee getting nearer and nearer. It brushed against my hair, but I didn't move. I think it liked the smell of shampoo. It swirled around as I held my breath and then luckily moved away. That was one thing Zack's world could never do away with — bees and bee stings. There were some things like bees and mosquitoes and hurricanes and tornadoes that would always be a problem, but the other bad things like people trying to blow each other up or hunger or pollution — those he was saying could actually change.

I liked the world he painted. It seemed to make sense, like it could really happen if enough people wanted it to. It was a world I'd always thought should exist but didn't know how to find before.

I heard the metal screen door bang, and Zack came back balancing sandwiches and a bag of chips. I didn't feel like talking and neither did he. I just ate and licked the ketchup spilling over the sides of my sandwich. I felt like I was hovering somewhere in the future, and I wasn't ready to crash back into the regular old present yet.

Zack suddenly put his sandwich down. He licked his fingers, ripped a piece of clean paper out of a pad he'd been doodling on, and began to write furiously. If I had tried to draw him at that moment, I would have shown smoke coming out of his ears, like a cartoon.

He picked the notebook up off the grass and made an elaborate show of hiding it behind his back and not letting me see where he put the new entry.

"Now you guess."

"How can I? There must be three hundred sheets of paper. How am I going to find it?"

"All I can say is you'll know when you do." He gave a grin and hummed a little tune as if to needle me.

I picked up the notebook and held it up so I could see the edge of all the papers. I was looking for one that stood up a little more than the others, but there was no even line of paper to go by. The whole edge of them was pretty ragged. Many of the articles had been inserted with the holes punched every which way.

I grabbed a handful of corn chips and contemplated what Sherlock would do. But right now I didn't want to act like a logical detective. I felt more like being a seagull flying where the wind took me and eventually arriving at my destination.

When I was finished eating, I turned back to "Inside America."

I found a section that said, "Solar Club Houses" and began to read. It was an interview that Zack had written up with his next-door neighbor in Syracuse who was a solar architect, and it was dated six years ago.

*Zack:* What are some things kids could do to learn more about solar energy?

*Daria:* Easy. Build solar club houses. Think about that. If you build one here in Syracuse and then you took a picture of you and your friends sitting inside it in the winter time, you could send the picture to a magazine and pretty soon kids all over the country would start creating their own.

Underneath the interview Zack had written, "Untried idea. Still on the back burner."

I stopped reading and began to daydream. Solar club houses! What would they look like? I was itching to draw one. And Zack was in fifth grade when he'd written that interview. I was surprised to think he'd kept his notebook that long. What if he had gone ahead and built one?

I imagined what Zack must have looked like as a fifth grader and then pictured him getting all of his friends involved in looking for old windows they could use for their club house. Then I imagined them with hammers prying off the boards on the south wall of an abandoned shack and putting in the windows. In my mind I drew a picture of Zack and his friends sitting inside the finished club house in the winter time with their hats and gloves off, all smiling.

"Blueprints," I said out loud, "That's what's inside this notebook, blueprints for all the different ways things could be." Just the way Sam had made up a blueprint for the way the attic would look when he was finished, Zack was drawing up blueprints for the world. "I wish lots of people could read this, Zack." I wanted them to be so excited about his ideas that they'd want to make them happen right now as much as I did.

I knew that the notebook wasn't really in the right shape to show to people yet. You couldn't just place it in the Larkspur Library and hope that people would react.

"Well, I wish there was another way to give people a picture of it all," I told him. Zack smiled mysteriously and didn't say a word.

So I turned back to my exploring. "Our Town." That was the section I'd been saving to read last. I flipped over the pages that were about his old home town of Syracuse and got right to Larkspur. I wondered if there would be anything there yet. One sheet of crisp new paper sat in that spot. New paper!

I had found the needle in the haystack.

LIKE TO DRAW?
CONCERNED ABOUT PEACE?
PEACE GROUP STARTING!
Join us the week before school starts, & bring your art supplies.
We'll make pictures of how we'd like the world to be and then ...
We'll put them on display for the town.
We'll meet every school vacation.
PEOPLE OF ALL AGES 8-18
ARE WELCOME
Location: I don't know yet.
Call Zack Clemmons

"Do you mean it?"

"Yup. Give me a day or two, and you'll see flyers about this all over Larkspur."

"Count me in. You got your first member," I told him.

"Member?" How could we have the group without you, Cassie? It was your drawings and, I don't know, the way you read today that gave me the inspiration for it."

It's not like Zack to flatter people, but still I looked at him again to see if he was kidding me.

He read my mind. "It's true, Cass."

"I could help deliver the flyers," I said, "and my parents might even print them at their shop for free."

He was so excited that at that moment the whole art display seemed as good as done as far as he was concerned.

When I biked home, speeding down the steep hill, I felt I could fly. I wondered how things like Zack's idea actually happened. Who would come to the group? Could we actually do it? I couldn't think of anyone I knew who'd be interested in joining except Louisa. Not Jill. Certainly not Sam. "Maybe Terry," I thought. "Yeah, Terry's got to come! I'll beg her to join!"

The next morning Zack called and asked me to come over and make a drawing to put on the flyer. No one else in my family was home so I left a message in the usual place, our blackboard in the kitchen. We always put our messages in code.

I thought about how to make a code with Zack's name. Then I drew a box with stars all round it, and inside the box I wrote:

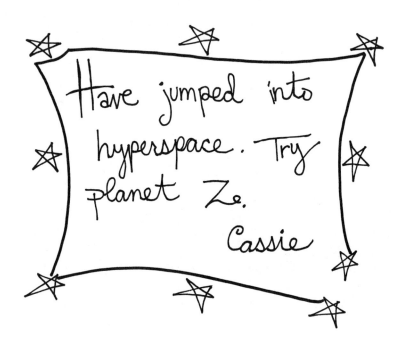

Have jumped into hyperspace. Try planet Ze.

Cassie

# In the Next War

♦ ♦ ♦

## BY ROBERT PRIEST

In the next war don't drop the bomb
Drop the excess wheat
Drop the sacks of grain
and the powdered milk we have too much of
Send our best men over
in daring flights
their bombers full
of fish eggs huge cheeses
and birthday cake icings
Don't machine gun our enemies
Rather let us scrape off our plates
and pelt them with leftover squash
We must inundate them with sauces and gravies
every day a new and better recipe
We have the technology to do this
We have the invisible aircraft
Now we must make an undetectable red rocket
a holy sky train that drops a mountain
of Kraft dinners and Coke
Bury the Kremlin in spaghetti
Minute Rice and mashed potatoes
This will be a new kind of war
It will take sacrifice and patience
Everyone will have to put something aside
for the enemy
We will start
with the ham and eggs
saving for the very end
our big weapon
the hamburger

# Mending Wall

◆ ◆ ◆

**BY**

**ROBERT**

**FROST**

Something there is that doesn't love a wall,
That sends the frozen-ground-swell under it
And spills the upper boulders in the sun,
And makes gaps even two can pass abreast.
The work of hunters is another thing:
I have come after them and made repair
Where they have left not one stone on a stone,
But they would have the rabbit out of hiding,
To please the yelping dogs. The gaps I mean,
No one has seen them made or heard them made,
But at spring mending-time we find them there.
I let my neighbor know beyond the hill;
And on a day we meet to walk the line
And set the wall between us once again.
We keep the wall between us as we go.
To each the boulders that have fallen to each.

And some are loaves and some so nearly balls
We have to use a spell to make them balance.
"Stay where you are until our backs are turned!"
We wear our fingers rough with handling them.
Oh, just another kind of outdoor game,
One on a side. It comes to little more:
There where it is we do not need the wall:
He is all pine and I am apple orchard.
My apple trees will never get across
And eat the cones under his pines, I tell him.
He only says, "Good fences make good neighbors."
Spring is the mischief in me, and I wonder
If I could put a notion in his head:
"*Why* do they make good neighbors? Isn't it
Where there are cows? But here there are no cows.
Before I built a wall I'd ask to know
What I was walling in or walling out,
And to whom I was like to give offense.
Something there is that doesn't love a wall,
That wants it down." I could say "Elves" to him,
But it's not elves exactly, and I'd rather
He said it for himself. I see him there,
Bringing a stone grasped firmly by the top
In each hand, like an old-stone savage armed.
He moves in darkness, as it seems to me,
Not of woods only and the shade of trees.
He will not go behind his father's saying,
And he likes having thought of it so well
He says again, "Good fences make good neighbors."

# Print Your Name Large

♦ ♦ ♦

**BY**

**JOAN**

**FINNIGAN**

**I** loved school! They say girls always do more than boys. I am sure I did more than all girls. Half a century later I still remember every detail of my kindergarten class at Percy Street School in Ottawa and, as for grade one where I learned to read, I can still see in my mind's eye and repeat for you the phonetic cards that lined the top of the blackboard on two sides of the room. I remember one time in that year being away from school ill and returning to find that the class had moved on to a new reader with these strange words like "cake" and "late" which made no sense at all when I sounded them out. In a state of panic I turned to a girl in the next row, a "repeater." "What are these words?" I gasped out to her, pointing to the phonetic rule-breakers. "The E makes the A say its own name," she whispered back to me. Oh magic, it worked! Nothing had been taken away from me. I was a very important person once more on the road to fulfilling my thirst for learning, to realizing my potential.

In my past twelve years of taping the old-timers of Ottawa Valley, I have met a goodly number who, in the process of giving me their life story, have said to me, "Oh, if I'd only gone to school!" Or, "If I'd only got more schooling my life would have been different!" I have met some who opened one of my proffered books so hesitantly that I knew intuitively they could not read. I have talked with others who simply said, "I can only read the pictures." Yes, a goodly number of times I was faced with what I consider to be the ultimate tragedy and the greater immorality—human potential unfulfilled.

But a number of years ago in my work with the NFB [National Film Board] I was involved in making a film on one of the precedent-setting rural classes for illiterates sponsored by the Ontario Government. "If you get to the main road, we'll pick you

up," the flyer said. And so, in the depths of January, from all age groups and all racial origins, through the snows on foot or sometimes behind the jingling sleigh-bells of horse-drawn cutters, the people who burned to learn to read and write got to the main road and were picked up for the Adult Learning Courses at Combermere. And there the feisty little teaching-nun, inspired by the intensity of the motivation of her pupils, took as her refrain a line which has been etched on my brain ever since: *You are a very important person! Print your name large."*

Yes, how many older people, bright, curious, intelligent, even brilliant, have I known in my oral history work, even in my own network of Valley clans, whose lack of education not only limited their development of potential but who were also keenly aware of the deprivation and the loss? And how many have I known who perhaps have learned the fundamentals of reading and writing but whose love of reading was not sufficiently kindled in their younger years to enrich their later years, who now sit, hands folded, by kitchen windows or lie, bored and hopeless on institutional beds, unable to make the myriad magical journeys of the imagination which reading makes possible?

Believe me, I never negate the experiential learning and wisdom of Native Peoples, and those who still live and work in the oral traditions. They have all kinds of riches of their own: the ability to live co-operatively; to do their own problem-solving often on the spot; to improvise and innovate for survival. These people took care of the earth — and still take care of the earth — far more than we of the so-called "civilized" and "educated" tribes of the Western World whose waste and greed, paradoxically, is bringing the whole earth to the brink of disaster. Throughout "The Global Village" the top priority today is the preservation of our environment and the solving of our ecological problems. All other issues pale beside such dire goals.

But, in a convoluted manner, learning to read is part of our preservation of the planet. For learning to read gives individuals their understanding of the Power of One, the Power of One to examine ideas, to ask questions, to demand political freedom, to exercise a vote, to claim individual rights to things like birth control, justice before the law, clean air. The Power of One developed by reading helps one to understand and believe in the power to change things. As the feisty little teaching-nun said in

Combermere: *"You are a very important person! Print your name large."*

Perhaps our sacrilegious North American waste of trees, pulp and paper can be counterbalanced by CODE's [Canadian Organization for Development Through Education] shipments of books and textbooks to Third World countries where all people, learning to read and write, will be given the Power of One to reject political confinements on freedom, to demand their human dignity, yes, perhaps even to find the strength to cry, "No! Stop!" when their environment is about to be pillaged and polluted.

In our "Global Village" the Power of One can effect change. Learning to read fills one with a sense of the Power of One. It is the people who believe in the Power of One who effect change. Everywhere let the E make the A say its own name.

# Literacy Program Gives New Hope and Pleasure to Family's Life

◆ ◆ ◆

**BY**

**FLORENCE LOYIE**

**L**ife is different at Donna Kratky's house these days.

Where she would have once told her children to go out and play or watch television when they were getting under foot, she now encourages them to read a book.

Her husband is more aware of current issues because he reads the newspaper, and to the children more often.

Kratky finds she likes to carry a book wherever she goes and spends her free time reading.

There was a time reading wasn't as important in the Kratky household. But that was before the Cappill family literacy project came into their lives.

The two-year, federally funded pilot project, operated through the Centre for Continuing Education, has completed its first year and is proving to be a success, says project manager Rolf Pritchard.

The project's goal is to promote literacy among poor, under-educated families, giving pre-schoolers in these families a fighting chance when they start school.

Studies show that the education levels of parents, particularly mothers, are related to how well their children do in school. Literate parents create a literate home environment.

But other parents, who are also poor, have difficulty achieving the same thing. Steps have to be taken to break children of these homes from the cycle, Pritchard says.

Programs such as Head Start, which provides support for pre-schoolers from low-income families, are useful. But whatever gains these children make are lost within a few years because literacy is not promoted in the home, he says.

The Cappill project is aimed at educating both disadvantaged pre-schoolers and their parents to create a home environment where literacy is promoted and flourishes, he says.

Kratky was one of nine mothers, with a total of 11 pre-schoolers between them, who enrolled in September 1991 in the project. At the time, Kratky read at the Grade 8 level. Her three oldest boys had difficulty reading, and it was likely her youngest son would follow suit.

Kratky will attend Concordia College this fall to continue her education. Her three oldest sons have improved their reading skills and the youngest boy is grasping ideas and concepts his brothers struggled with when they were his age.

The project has made an unexpected difference in her family's lives, Kratky says.

"We have come a long way...We are picking out books and I get them to read to each other. That is something I never did before. It was go outside and play or watch TV. Now it's go and read a book."

The program has made her realize parents have a responsibility to make sure their children understand the importance of education. "If the parents don't stress that, then the kids don't get the message."

One of her goals is to study Cree at Concordia so she can reach native elders and help them make young people understand the importance of education, says Kratky, a treaty Indian.

# No Place Like Home

◆ ◆ ◆

**FROM**

**WORLD VISION**

**CANADA**

## STREET NUMBERS

Some stats on the world wide shelter crisis.

- Over one billion people in our world live without adequate shelter.[1] (For a definition, see "The Shelter Checklist.")
- People without adequate shelter make up about one-third of the population in developing countries — about 1.3 billion people.[1]
- There are over 100 million refugees world wide, uprooted and displaced by war and natural disasters. Most live in temporary camps without shelter.
- In some large cities of the developing world, as many as half of the people live in slums.[1]
- In Calcutta, one-third of the population—about 4 million people— survives in temporary huts, each shared by an average of five families. That's almost twice the population of Toronto.[2]

## WHY DON'T THEY HAVE SHELTER?

Many reasons and one reason.

Meet a few of the people behind the numbers.

**MAREIKA** and her family moved from Jakarta on the island of Java to the forests of West Kalimantan because the Indonesian government paid them to resettle and farm there. They thought they'd left the poverty of the city behind. But now they live in a leaky two-room shack and barely have enough to eat. This year's crops are failing because the soil of the piece of jungle they cleared three years ago is exhausted.

**JOSEPH** lives under a tarp in a garbage dump in Nairobi. He used to work a small farm with his brothers, growing coffee. But people in the West are drinking less coffee and the price has been dropping for years. Joseph couldn't make enough to feed his family, so he came to the city to find work. But there isn't much.

**LINO** lives on the street in Luanda, Angola. He's here because his mother and father were killed in a battle between government soldiers and rebels that destroyed their village.

**DAMIANA** and her family live in a one-room shack on a hillside in Rio de Janeiro. There's no water or sewer. They're here because the farm land the family has worked for several generations has been taken over to become part of a big plantation to grow crops for export.

**FATIMA** lives in a make-shift tent in a refugee camp located in the countryside of Sudan. She's here because drought has left her farm without a crop for three years, and she has no money left for new seed. At least in the camp she can eat.

**MOUDUD** lives in the remains of his mud hut on the coast of Bangladesh. A tropical storm destroyed his home last week. Even though he knows it's dangerous to stay, he's still here because he can't afford to live anywhere else.

Many factors play a part in these stories.

- Lack or loss of land. Farmers can lose their land by having it taken by force, by selling it in desperation, or by watching it dwindle as successive generations divide an old family farm.
- Falling crop prices. Governments and powerful multinational companies can keep crop prices low to stay competitive—keeping farm incomes low as well.
- War. Conflict can force entire populations into cities or refugee camps in the countryside.
- Resettlement and migration. With the aim of economic development, governments can encourage large numbers of their people to settle in areas that may not be able to support them.
- Natural disaster. Floods and cyclones destroy homes; droughts and famines force people to leave them.
- Environmental deterioration. Long-term deterioration of soil and water conditions can force people from farms that have provided a home for generations.

But in the final analysis, the real reason the people in these stories are without adequate shelter is that they are poor. Poverty made them vulnerable to big — and at times unjust — natural and human forces. In most cases, those forces have uprooted them and forced them to leave whatever shelter they had.

> **THE SHELTER CHECKLIST**
> What makes a shelter "adequate"? To be adequate, according to the United Nations' definition[3], a shelter must:
> ✓ provide protection from the weather.
> ✓ provide access to clean water and to sanitation.
> ✓ provide personal safety and a supportive emotional environment.
> ✓ be located within reasonable reach of work, school and medical facilities.
> ✓ not cost more than people can reasonably afford.

## IT CAME FROM THE SWAMP
### How one African shantytown transformed itself[4]

Nineteen-year-old Akoa had come to live with his uncle in Makepe, one of the oldest shantytowns in Douala, the most populous city in Cameroon. Soon after his arrival, Akoa's uncle took him to the top of a hill overlooking Makepe, and proudly told him the story of its transformation.

"Akoa, take a look at the area around you and try to imagine what it was like 25 years ago. The hill you are sitting on was the only dry land around here. Everything was swamp.

"After the civil war, when we got our independence, thousands of farmers left the countryside to take refuge in the city. We settled here. They gave me a piece of marshland about 15 paces long by about 10 wide. Each family got only that much.

"The first thing to do was to dry out the land. At night, while I watched the land to protect against thieves, my wife would go down to the road with a hoe and would fill her bucket with earth and gravel. She could make about 20 trips a night. This is how we dried and filled the land.

"Next came the house. Back in the village, we built huts with mud and bamboo, but here we had to find other materials. We used old sheet metal, tea crates, old boards, anything we could get our hands on. Our first hut had two rooms.

"Two years passed. We wanted a school for our children, a place to study that was sheltered from the cold and rain, so it had to be a stone building. The government agreed to provide the sheet metal and cement, but we had to find the stone.

"On Sunday mornings, each person who lived in the district had to bring a large rock or stone to the hill. And that is what we used to build the school.

"Several years passed. The swamp came to be completely inhabited. But during the rainy season, each hut became a tiny island in a sea of muddy water. It was a danger to our health. My first son died of cholera. So we had to dry up the whole swamp.

"We set up a co-operative. It took us five years to dry up the swamp completely. We had to build dikes to keep the water from flooding us again.

"Little by little, my wife and I saved, until we had enough to build a new hut out of cement blocks. We built the new one around the old one, and just before we put on the roof, we tore the old one down.

"We also got running water that year. The government put in wells every 500 metres and installed communal showers. The next year we got a dispensary in the area, and the next year, the government decided to pave the road leading here. Until that time, we used to have to walk for three kilometres to get to the closest bus stop. Now we have bus service right into the district.

"And that, Akoa, is how Makepe became what it is today. It took time and the help of everyone to achieve it. A single straw cannot sweep a courtyard!"

1 The Global Strategy for Shelter to the Year 2000. United Nations Centre for Human Settlement (Habitat), Nairobi, 1990
2 United Nations Population Division, 1986
3 Social Development Overview, Vol. 5 No. 1, Autumn 1987, page 2
4 Excerpted and adapted from "Changing My Shantytown," Under the Same Sun, Fall 1989, Canadian International Development Agency

# Child Labor Aids 'Miracle' of Asia

♦ ♦ ♦

**BY**

**DAVE**

**TODD**

**I**t's the dark side of Asia's economic miracle. From Bombay to Bangkok, Sri Lanka to the South China Sea, the phenomenal growth of a rapidly industrializing continent is being fueled by the cheap labor of millions of children.

Construction sites and factories, tropical plantations and sweatshops in the back streets of the great cities — these are the joyless haunts of illiterate, ill-cared for girls and boys living on the margins of "globalizing" economies geared to producing goods for world export markets.

Throughout Asia, whether it's Pakistan, Nepal or the Philippines, most child work remains agricultural.

But across South and Southeast Asia, there has been an explosion in the number of urban child laborers as one country after another attempts to undercut its neighbor in the war to sell low-cost consumer goods to the West and Asia's wealthier nations.

In 1991, the volume of exports from Asia rose almost 13 per cent, four times faster than the growth of trade worldwide, says the International Monetary Fund. From 1990 to 2000, average annual export growth in East Asia is expected to approach 10 per cent. In South Asia, exports will grow by nearly eight per cent.

Yet the critical role that Asia's working children have played in propelling their countries into this new world economic order receives little attention from policy-makers and analysts.

Indonesia and Thailand boast two of the East's largest economic growth rates over the past decade — they are also notorious for neglecting their most vulnerable citizens.

"Children in electric light bulb factories in Indonesia work from 7 a.m. to 3 p.m., six days a week for $3 U.S. a week," the

International Labor Organization reports in a new study of child labor.

It's worse elsewhere in the region. In Bangladesh, children as young as eight spend up to 16 hours a day cutting cloth for shirts and blouses that end up in Canadian department stores. During the first three months, they are paid nothing. After that, wages start at $9 or $10 a month.

In the Indian state of Tamil Nadu, small boys employed in tanning factories at 50 cents a day work 10-hour shifts, without protective masks or gloves, applying poisonous, skin-burning chemicals to animal hides to cure them for leather-making.

"Children are specifically suited for this work," says Virgil D'Sami, head of Year of the Child Development Trust. "The skins are put inside rotation drums and mixed with the chemicals, and are removed by children entering the drums.

"The children are forced to remain inside the drums for considerable periods."

A survey by Thailand's National Youth Promotion Committee found that the vast majority of the country's pre-teen and teenage laborers have never had a routine health examination.

Many Asian nations have refused to ratify the United Nations Convention on the Rights of the Child, whose passage in 1989 was designed to herald a new era in the lives of the world's children.

The government of Indonesia won't even let the U.N. Children's Emergency Fund (UNICEF) collect social statistics or health care data.

"In the area of child labor, Indonesia is totally restrictive," says Panudda Boonpala, Asia's best known child rights advocate.

"But I believe eventually we will be able to find a way. Even with the toughest people, I think you can eventually get through if the issue is mistreating children. It is a measure of a human being."

# Trying Not to See

♦ ♦ ♦

BY

CATHY

BEVERIDGE

"It all starts here." Mr. Clarke pinches the stem of a lacy leaf between his fingernails. Immediately, the class grows quiet. I glance up quickly as does Stefan. Behind me, a voice groans, anticipating another dramatic science lesson. I grin, stealing a glance at Heather, and try to focus on what Mr. Clarke is saying. But my gaze wanders instead, and I find myself studying Stefan as I have done since his arrival at our school this morning. I note the harsh concentration of his eyes, the tense uprightness of his shoulders and the constant pressure of his fingertips on the desktop. There is something hauntingly familiar about it all.

In a dramatic gesture, Mr. Clarke flips the leaf over and points at a small, dark patch near its base. "A tiny egg, like this one, adheres to the underside of a leaf. Inside, a small creature is growing bigger and darker until finally, the egg bursts." He releases the leaf and watches silently as it flutters to the floor. I, too, am silent, watching, but trying not to see. Stefan's hand twitches as Mr. Clarke reaches gingerly into a beaker and holds the creature on his index finger up to the light. A small, striped caterpillar creeps into the brightness, balancing delicately on a leaf. Instinctively, the tiny caterpillar uses its two rows of creeper feet to maintain its balance.

I see it then, the almost imperceptible turning of his head. Stefan looks first to his right, then his left, but the eyes of the class watch the caterpillar. Mr. Clarke's voice drones on and, finally, Stefan, who I've heard is alone in this world, seems to escape to another. I know intuitively where he has gone, for his past surely resembles my own.

The wind knocks against the window pane as Father spreads his newspaper across the wooden tabletop and forces a low whistle through the space between his upper teeth. I stand before him in the thin light waiting for his rough hands to clasp my face in his habitual goodnight gesture. Then Petar will tuck me into our hard, cold bed in the next room, and, if he can manage, press a bit of bread into my hand so my stomach will also sleep.

*I shut my eyes against the memory as Mr. Clarke's narrative continues. "Its tiny stomach is ravenous, and in seconds, the caterpillar has begun its hunt for food. It creeps slowly at first, but quickly discovers how to maneuver its body in search of tender leaves."*

It is New Year's Day and candles burn in the kitchen, for once again our power is being rationed. There is tea with sugar which Mother sets out, glancing sideways in my direction. The sugar was my gift and I will not tell her how I got it. Grandmother's hands, worn, like the shawl around her shoulders, clutch a steaming mug. Father tells her that the eighties will bring many changes to our country. There will be an election and maybe a new government. Grandmother nods and even Petar smiles silently. I am warmed by their optimism.

*"With each passing day, the caterpillar grows, climbing higher and higher amongst fragrant flowers and swaying stalks. Then one day, its skin feels tight. The little caterpillar has outgrown its striped suit. Breathing deeply, the caterpillar begins to swallow air, puffing its body up like a balloon until its skin splits. Old and wrinkled, the skin falls off."*

It is election day, a day full of spring promises. We crowd around the radio as the results are announced. The government has been defeated. There is much joy as neighbors gather to celebrate, much talk of full cupboards and better wages. Each day, I race home from school awaiting the good news. But as the cold winter subsides, it is obvious that the promises were as empty as my stomach.

*"The caterpillar emerges in a new striped skin. With each passing day, it eats, and grows, now moving with new confidence across gardens of green. In the morning it seeks out others wearing similar striped suits and in the hot afternoon sun, it rests."*

A group of young people have begun meeting in the evenings. I follow Petar despite my mother's warnings. There is talk of democracy, free elections, an end to the regime. Mother and Father are anxious, but they listen thoughtfully to Petar's reports. Other countries have organized peaceful demonstrations and opposing political parties.

Petar says that we must try to do the same.

*"But this kingdom is not without danger, and very soon a hungry bird circles above the caterpillar. Instinctively, it hides its striped suit among the heavy green foliage of its home, and escapes the keen eye of the bird."*

Someone has been careless. Our meeting is just beginning when we hear the voices of the military police. In moments we are gone, their heavy footsteps unable to follow us into our childhood hiding places.

*"It is not long before the bird returns and stands poised above the unsuspecting caterpillar. Unable to escape this time, it rears up, orange horns protruding from its head, its glands giving off a strong scent. The bird retreats and the caterpillar continues its own search, knowing that its enemy will return in time."*

It is our first public demonstration and we shiver despite the heat of the city. I stand on the steps of the government buildings beside Petar, as others assemble in the square. The speeches begin, and the crowd, so much larger than we expected, catches fire. I jump to my feet, infused by their energy. Then suddenly the military police are there, armed with heavy clubs. They try to arrest Nikolas, who has the megaphone, but the crowd begins to chant. One of them grabs the megaphone and orders the crowd to go home, but nobody moves. Nikolas struggles and a club is raised. Petar jumps to his aid. I jump after him, but find a hand on my arm. I wriggle free as the crowd advances. There are too many of us and soon they retreat. We flash the victory sign, but the next morning, the police arrive to arrest Petar.

*"Throughout the warm days, the caterpillar continues to grow, shedding its skin as the need arises. Behind it, it leaves a trail of eaten greens and flowers. Then, one day, it stops eating. It creeps along the ground, moving quickly with an innate sense of urgency, searching its habitat for some place that is tall, firm and, above all, safe."*

They go underground on my thirteenth birthday. Mother and Father are terrified when I tell them that I will act as a go-between, but they understand. For months, in the guise of a delivery boy, I carry messages, until I creep home in the darkness and find the police vehicle waiting. I disappear into the shadows and return at dawn a week later. My parents are distraught. My grandmother is very ill, but it is unsafe for me to stay at home. Five days later, Father sends word to me. Grandmother had died, and he has a plan.

*"Finally, the caterpillar locates a dead branch of a tree, hidden amongst the foliage and climbs up. There, it makes a silky sling that encircles its body and holds it safely to the branch. Suspended against the wood, the caterpillar stretches and curls until its suit of skin splits. Wiggling and shaking, it disengages itself from the striped skin and rests."*

Uncle Ted and Aunt Sophie from Canada have returned for the funeral. After the service, Uncle Ted will drive Grandmother's body back to her childhood town to be buried. I will go with them. From where I crouch in the shadows, I can see the open doors of the chapel. I spot Mother standing inside the chapel but there is no time for good-byes. Beside the chapel, the police are questioning Uncle Ted. I begin to perspire and then I see Father standing beside the hearse. He spots me immediately and motions me over. I move quickly. Father opens the door of the hearse and lifts a blanket covering a small space in the back. I hide beneath it. I wait. I clench my teeth and will my heart to stop pounding as the coffin is slid into the hearse. I close my mind to the horror that grips me. I hear the icy voices of the police and then the rumble of the car engine. I weep silently.

*"This is the last skin the caterpillar will shed, for this time it has run out of skin. Now it resembles the small twig from which it is suspended."*

Nobody questions my forged passport or the story that I am Ted and Sophie's son from Calgary, returning from my grandmother's funeral. And suddenly, I am. Each day, I wish that I could shut myself away; I am so different from the others. They ask, at first, about my homeland and my family. Sometimes I do not know the words to answer and sometimes I know the words will be too painful, so I pretend not to understand.

*"The caterpillar has now entered the pupating stage. From the outside, it appears to be a small, brown, lifeless twig. But inside, the caterpillar is changing, growing long legs, wide, colourful wings. Soon the small brown twig begins to darken and the outlines of a black body with black wings can be seen."*

Eventually, I begin to imitate them, to learn English and quietly change my way of dressing. My uncle takes me to a professional hockey game where I eat hotdogs and popcorn. A boy in my class becomes my friend. He teaches me to play football. We ride our bicycles, wrestle in the snow and talk the summer months away.

*"One morning, the twig-like shell bursts and a wet, crumpled*

*creature emerges, dangling from the tree branch with its long legs.
Slowly, four wings dotted with bold colours unfold while the creature,
now a butterfly, swallows air, pumping blood into its wings to dry and
harden them."*

By grade nine, my friends no longer ask about my past and there
are moments when I think that even I have forgotten. They have
changed my name to Mike. At the Christmas dance, Heather agrees to
be my girlfriend. I make the basketball team. I am one of them.

*"Feeling its strength come back, it can no longer resist the call of a
warm breeze. Sailing upwards, the butterfly drifts above the gardens
in search of bright flowers. It lands gently on the soft petals, tasting
sweetness with its feet, and sipping the nectar through its long, curled
tongue."*

The intercom buzzes as my eyes sweep across the classroom.
Stefan's pencil moves aimlessly in his hand; he has not even heard the
interruption. I force myself to look away as Mr. Clarke continues.

*"Throughout the summer, the butterfly flits above its world, eating
and resting in the warm sunshine. A search for more nectar brings it
into contact with more butterflies of the same species and they travel
together, darting in the air."*

Mr. Clarke pauses to pass out our assignment. Stefan's eyes stare
blankly at the page, a mirror of hopeless frustration. I scratch my
name violently on the page, breaking my pencil tip and trying to ignore
the voice that screams inside my head. Things are different now. I am
not the same person as I was then.

*"I have just described to you an incredible transformation. A lowly
caterpillar creeping amongst the underbrush has emerged as a beautiful butterfly. But, again, nature has an ironic twist. The carefree creatures flitting and darting amongst themselves cannot forget their
beginnings. As their lives draw to a close, they search out a lacy green
leaf and deposit the eggs that will eventually become humble caterpil-
lars."*

I skim the assignment, suddenly realizing that I have missed most
of Mr. Clarke's lesson. Stefan stares at the page and then folds it in
half. I stand and make my way past him to the pencil sharpener. He
looks up suddenly as I pass. It is no use. I crouch beside his desk.
"Mikhail," I say, by way of introduction and for a brief second, I see my
reflection in the hopeful glitter of his eyes.

# The Rebellion
# of the
# Magical Rabbits

♦ ♦ ♦

**BY**

**ARIEL**

**DORFMAN**

**W**hen the wolves conquered the land of the rabbits, the first thing the leader of the pack did was to proclaim himself King. The second was to announce that the rabbits had ceased to exist. Now and forever it would be forbidden to even mention their name.

Just to be on the safe side, the new Wolf King went over every book in his realm with a big black pencil, crossing out words and tearing out pictures of cottontails until he was satisfied that not a trace of his enemies remained.

But an old gray fox who was his counselor brought bad news.

"The birds, Your Wolfiness, insist that they have seen some...some of those creatures. From on high."

"So how come I don't see anything from way up here, on my throne?" asked the Wolf.

"In times like these," answered the fox, "people have got to see to believe."

"Seeing is believing? Bring me that monkey who takes photos, the one who lives nearby. I'll teach those birds a lesson."

The monkey was old and weak.

"What can the Wolf of all Wolves want with me?" he asked, looking at his wife and daughter.

The little girl had an answer. "He must want you to take a picture of the rabbits, Dad."

"Quiet, quiet," said her mother. "Rabbits don't exist."

But the little monkey knew that rabbits did exist. It was true that, since the howling wolves had invaded the country, the rabbits no longer came to visit her as they had before. But in her dreams she continued hearing the green rain of their voices singing nearby, reflecting in her head as if she were a pond under the moonlight, and when she awoke there was always a small gift beside her bed. Walls and closed doors were like water for the rabbits.

"That's why I sleep well," said the little girl. "That's why that General Wolf must need the photo. To keep nightmares away. You'll bring me a picture of them someday, won't you, Dad?"

The monkey felt fear crawl up and down his fur. "Send this little girl to her room," he told his wife, "until she understands that there are certain things we just don't talk about."

The King of the Wolves was not in the best of moods when the monkey came in. "You're late. And I'm in a hurry. I need photographs of each important act in my life. And all my acts, let me tell you, are supremely important....Can you guess what we're going to do with those pictures? You can't? We're going to put one on every street, inside every bush, in every home. I'll be there, watching each citizen with my very own eyes. You'd better pity those who don't have the latest events of my life hung up on their walls. And you know who is going to distribute each picture? You don't know?"

The monkey was trembling so hard that no words came out.

"The birds, ugly monkey. Now they'll bite their own beaks before they twitter around with any nonsense about rabbits. And we'll tie an endless cord to their legs, so they can't escape. Understand?"

The monkey understood so well that his trembling paw immediately clicked the shutter of the camera, taking the first picture.

"Go," roared the Wolf, "and develop it. I want it on every wall in the kingdom."

But when the photographer returned some minutes later, he did not dare to enter the throne room, and asked one of the soldiers to call the counselor. Without a word, the monkey passed him the picture he had just taken.

The fox blinked once, and then blinked again. In a corner of the photo, far from the muscular, ferocious figure of the King—who had both arms up in the air as if he had just won a boxing championship—appeared what was without any doubt the beginning of an ear, the ear of someone who had insolently come to spy on the whole ceremony.

"You blind monkey!" fumed the fox. "How come you didn't notice that this...this thing was there? Can't you focus that camera of yours?"

"If it could get into the picture," the monkey answered, "it was because you and your guards let it get close."

"It won't happen again," the counselor promised. "Rub out that...ear before His Wolfishness finds out."

From his bag, the monkey took out a special liquid that he used to erase any detail that might bother a client. The intruding ear began to disappear as if it had never existed.

The King of the Wolves was pleased with the portrait and ordered it sent all over the realm. Two hours later he personally went on an inspection tour to make sure that not a window was without a picture of his large, gleaming, dangerous grin. "Not bad," he said, "but this photo is already getting old. People should see my latest deeds. Take another. Quick. Show me scaring these pigeons—right away. And bring it to me immediately. You took too long last time."

But the monkey wasn't able to comply this time either. Once again he had the counselor called secretly.

"Again?" asked the fox. "It happened again?"

Except that now it was worse than an indiscreet ear. A whole corner of the new picture was filled with the unmistakable face of...yes, there was no denying it, of a rabbit winking an eye in open defiance of the nearby guards.

"We've got to tighten security," muttered the fox. "Meanwhile, erase that invader."

"Wonderful," shouted the King Wolf when finally he was given the picture. "Look at the frightened faces of the pigeons trying to escape. I want a million copies. I want them on milk cartons and on the coupons inside cereals....Onward. Onward. Let's go and smash up a dam. Come on, monkey. Fame awaits us both."

The beavers had been working summer and winter for three years on a beautiful dam that would allow them to irrigate a distant valley.

The Wolf of Wolves climbed a tree. "I want you to shoot the precise moment when my feet crash into the middle of the dam, monkey. If you miss the shot, next time I'll fall on top of you and then I'll have to get myself another photographer. Are you ready?"

Not only was the monkey ready, so was the counselor. The fox was breathing down the old monkey's back, peering over his shoulder, watching, listening. Nothing could escape those vigilant, darting eyes. Not a fuzzy ear would dare to make its appearance.

So neither the monkey nor the fox could believe it when, a bit later, they saw at the bottom of the picture a rabbit lolling on his side as if he were relaxing at a picnic. Next to him, another rabbit had raised her paw and was boldly thumbing her nose.

"This is an epidemic," said the fox. "And let me tell you, our lives are in danger."

"Let's start erasing," the monkey said wearily.

"You erase. I'll get a squadron of buzzards and hawks. They see all animals, even the quick and the small."

His Wolfhood the King yelped with pleasure when he saw the picture. It portrayed him at the exact moment he was breaking the backbone of the beavers' dam. In the distance, families of beavers could be seen fleeing. There was not a single shadow of a rabbit.

"Send it out! A strong country is an educated country, a country that always is tuned in to the latest news. What are we going to do now for some fun?"

"We could rest," the monkey suggested, his paws peeling from the harsh erasing fluid.

The Wolf looked at him as if he were a stone.

"And who asked you for an opinion? I'm in charge here. That's why I was born with these teeth, and you'd better pray you never have to feel them crunching your bones. Onward. We are the future, the morrow, the dawn! We'll go on until there's no more light."

But in each new photo, the rabbits became more plentiful, audacious, and saucy. His Wolfinity the King destroyed sugar mills, shook squirrels out of their trees and hid their nuts, stripped ducks of their feathers, drove sheep off cliffs, drilled holes in the road so that horses would break their legs, unveiled new cages and old dungeons...and the more his frightening yellow eyes flickered, the more innumerable were the rabbits of every color that frolicked in the margins of the photographs. Even the clouds seemed full of fur and whiskers and cottontails.

"Hey, birdie," jeered the Supreme Wolf, grabbing a swallow about to fly off with a bag overflowing with pictures, "what tune are you singing now, featherhead? Who's that in the center of the picture, huh? Who's the King?"

The bird held his beak tight, so that not even a peep could come out.

"Lights, camera, action, monkey!" the Monarch demanded. "Call this: WOLF KING RECEIVES HOMAGE FROM A MESSENGER."

The monkey obeyed, but could hardly hide his despair. Though nobody ever saw the rebels when the photos were taken, they were always there when it was time to show them, nibbling lettuce at the very feet of the biggest and baddest of wolves.

"Exterminate them," hissed the fox, who had ordered a stronger, more acid liquid. "Don't leave even a twitch of a nose."

But the pictures were beginning to look defective. There were blank spaces everywhere. The monkey knew that the only solution was to convince His Wolfiness to sit up high on an elevated throne. Since rabbits live underground, they wouldn't be able to wiggle their way into the frame of the photograph.

The King, fortunately, was delighted with the idea. "I'll look more impressive up here. And I can keep an eye on those birds. What a surprise for my subjects when they find my new picture at breakfast, right? So get here early, monkey, do you hear?"

When the exhausted monkey dragged himself home, his fingers hurting from the terrible liquid, the latest photograph of the King had just been plastered on the front door of his house. Just at that moment, a soldier was leaving.

"No cause for alarm, Mr. Monkey," the soldier laughed. "Just a routine inspection to see if anybody is sabotaging His Wolfhood's pictures."

The monkey rushed inside. "Our daughter? Is she all right? Did she say anything?"

"I'm fine, Dad," the little girl said. "Those wolves are gone, aren't they? And you brought me that special photo—you know, the one I asked you for?"

The monkey felt as if from all four walls, from all four pictures on the four walls, the eight eyes of the Biggest of Wolves were watching each word he might say.

"Let your father rest," said her mother. "The only pictures he's taken are the ones we've put up in the house, like good citizens."

But the next morning, the monkey was awakened by his child's kiss. She put her lips near his ears and whispered something so softly that only he could hear it: "Thank you. It's the best present you could ever give me. You're a magical dad."

"Thanks? Thanks for what?"

She motioned almost imperceptibly toward the wall from which the photo of the Wolf King ruled. Her father opened his eyes wide. In one of the corners of that picture, like the sun rising over the mountains, he could just glimpse, in the act of making their gradual but glorious appearance, a pair of, yes, of course, a pair of soft, pink, pointed ears.

The monkey jumped out of bed. The liquid he had applied did not work permanently. The rabbits had needed the whole night to sneak back into the pictures, but somehow they had managed it.

"I think they knew I was scared," the little girl murmured, "and came to see me while I slept."

Her father dressed in less time than it takes a chill to run up a spine and scurried to the palace without stopping for breakfast. Was this happening only at their house or could the same invasion have taken place everywhere in the kingdom? If so, how could the rabbits be removed from so many portraits?

His Wolfiness was still in bed, but the counselor was already pacing about, biting the tip of his tail. "It's a plague," he said, "but, fortunately, it is already under control. The offending pictures have been burned. As for you..."

"I swear that I—"

"Not a word from you," interrupted the fox. "It's lucky those creatures don't exist. Imagine the damage they'd cause if they really existed. But enough talk. What we need now is a new photo to replace the ones that are contaminated."

They rushed to the new throne, which was now set up on top of four colossal wooden legs, out of reach of the spreading virus of the mischievous ears.

"I want two shots," His Wolfhood demanded, "one of me ascending my throne and another of me sitting on it, enjoying the fresh air. And send them abroad too, so those silly foreign papers will stop attacking me."

This time, when the photos were developed, there was no trouble. Not so much as a carrot of a sign of a rabbit.

"Didn't I tell you? Didn't I tell you they don't exist?" The counselor was jubilant. "It was just a matter of your focusing the camera properly."

For the next few days, there were no more unpleasant surprises. The Wolf of Wolves felt happy, high above the heads of the multitude. He let his lieutenants run things while he posed for pictures giving commands, delivering speeches, signing laws. He examined the shots carefully, however. "Congratulations," he said. "You're being more careful, monkey. It seems you're learning your trade just by being near me. I don't see any more of those whitish spots that spoiled my first pictures."

But one morning, the monkey was again awakened by his daughter's voice. "They're back, Dad," she whispered in his ears. "Those pictures you took sure are magical."

In one set of photos, at the foot of the towering throne, a small army of rabbits was biting, chewing, and splintering the wooden legs. Their teeth worked patiently, and they stopped their work only now and again to wave to the spectators.

The counselor was waiting. The monkey could see his fur ruffling and swelling like a swarm of bees.

"How many this time?" the monkey asked.

"The photos are being taken care of," the fox said grimly. "But the birds have got wind of what happened, and now they're telling everyone that those...those awful animals exist. And His Wolfinity is beginning to suspect something. 'Why are those birds so happy, so shrill?' he asks. I told him they're just a bunch of featherbrains, full of hot air."

"What did he answer?" asked the monkey.

The King had announced that balloons are full of hot air too and that they could be popped. If those birds didn't keep quiet, he would make them disappear.

But the counselor had another idea: The Wolf of All Wolves should tie a recording of one of his latest speeches around the necks of the birds. They would have to carry not only the photos, but also the King's words, all over his kingdom. Nobody would be able to hear any of their songs.

"Hearing is believing," trumpeted His Wolfiness. "We'll give them a taste of some hymns, some military marches, some lessons in history, economics, and ethics."

The old monkey's life became unbearable. Not even the recorded howls of the King and his chorus of warlike beasts could stop the timid appearance, in the next photo, of an inquisitive nose, a pair of furry ears, some white whiskers, and something hungry gnawing away the legs of the throne.

The fox replaced the chief officer of the royal guard with a boa constrictor straight from the jungle of a neighboring country. He put small, hundred-eyed spiders in strategic places throughout the Wolfdom. One day he ordered half the population to shave off their shiny fur so that no spy could hide in it. To punish the cows, accused of uttering subversive moos, he commanded that their milk be soured. And finally, he raised the volume of the King's broadcasts. But in spite of these efforts, there began to be heard a persistent, rowdy, merry sound, the clicking of thousands of tiny teeth, the burbling of an underground stream.

The monkey felt dizzy.

The rhythm was maddening. During the night, the legs of the throne, spindlier by the minute, were reinforced grudgingly by woodpeckers who would have much preferred to take the throne apart. The monkey had to rely on every photographic trick of the trade, now erasing, now trimming with scissors, disguising ears so they looked like shadows and shadows so they looked like wallpaper. He even began using old portraits of the King, trying to make them seem like recent ones.

Until one night, when it was very late, the old monkey was awakened by an angry hand that shook him from his slumber. It was the counselor, flanked by a fierce escort of soldiers. The Lord Wolf had sent for him.

The whole house was up by now. The little girl watched her father begin dressing.

"Say hello to His Foxcellency," said the monkey.

"Dad," she said, and it was astonishing that she did not speak in a low, fearful voice anymore, as if the armed guards were not even there, "today you've got to bring me that picture I asked for."

"A picture?" The counselor showed interest. "A picture of what, of whom?"

The child continued to ignore him. "Today you'll bring me a photo of the rabbits, right, Dad? For my wall?"

The mother monkey touched the girl's head as if she had fever. "Hasn't your father told you that rabbits don't exist? Haven't we shut you up in your room for telling lies?"

"They exist," the girl announced. "Everybody knows they exist."

"Just as I suspected," said the counselor. "Let's go."

The Wolfiest of Wolves was waiting for them atop his throne. Around each leg, hundreds of guards and snakes kept watch.

"Monkey, you are a traitor," thundered the King. "Your photos are being used by people who say that strange and malicious creatures—

who are non-existent as everyone knows—are conspiring this very night to overthrow my rule. They say my throne trembles and my dynasty will topple. Is there any evidence that my throne trembles? Does anybody dare say so?" And he yowled like a hundred jet fighters in the air. "We'll start by making a recording of that sound. And you, you monkey, you're going to help me stamp out these rumors. Touching is believing. You are going to make me a wide-angle, three-dimensional picture that will cover all walls. In color. Because I am going to crown myself Emperor of the Wolves, the Supreme Wolferor. And if a single wretched rabbit shows its snout, I will make you eat the photos, one by one, a million of them, and then I'll eat you and not only you, but your wife and your daughter, and all the monkeys in this country. Now. Take that picture."

The monkey stuck his quaking head under the black cloth behind his camera and focused on the throne. He let out a little moan. Up till then, the rabbits had appeared only later, when the picture was developed. But here they were now, directly in front of his lens, ungovernable and carefree, gnawing away, biting not only the wood of the throne, but also the swords of the astonished guards and the very rattles of the rattlesnakes.

"What's the matter?" bellowed the future Wolferor, who was not looking downward so his profile would be perfect for posterity.

The monkey moved the camera nearer the throne, hoping the rabbit army would not come out in the picture. The rabbits moved faster than he did. They were clambering up the legs, one on top of the other as if they were monkeys or birds. The soldiers tried to frighten them away in silence, unwilling to attract the attention of the King, but the invaders were too agile. The Wolves kept bumping into one another and hitting each other over the head. The monkey realized that a contingent of birds had arrived from above, winging freely through the air, without a cord tied to them or a recording.

"Hurry up!" ordered the Wolf of all Wolves.

The monkey closed his eyes very tightly. It was better not to witness what was going to happen. At the very moment he clicked the shutter, he heard a deafening noise. He knew what he was going to see when he opened his eyes, but still could not believe it: Like an old elm tree rotten to the core, the throne had come crashing to the ground along with the King of Wolves, guards, snakes, counselor, and all. The monkey blinked. There at the foot of his tripod lay the Biggest, Baddest, the Most Boastful Wolf in the Universe. His ribs were broken, his black fur was torn by the fall, his yellow eyes were reddened, and he was wailing in pain.

"Monkey," squeaked the would-be Wolferor of the World, "this picture…you have my permission not to publish it."

At that moment, all the lights in the palace went out. The monkey was paralyzed. He did not know where to go. Then, as if someone in the darkness were suddenly shining a light on a pathway, he knew what he must do. He grabbed his camera and his bag, and clutching them to his chest like a treasure, he fled.

His daughter was waiting for him at the door of the house.

"Wait," he said to her. "Wait. I've brought you something." And without another word, he raced into his darkroom to develop the last picture as quickly as possible.

When he came out a few minutes later, his daughter and wife were standing on chairs, taking down the pictures of the Wolf King.

"Here," the old monkey said to his daughter, blinking in the bright light. "Here, this is the picture you've been asking for all this time. I've finally brought you your present."

"Thanks, Dad," the little girl said. "But I don't need it anymore."

She pointed around the room and toward the street and across the fields where the sun was beginning to rise.

The world was full of rabbits.

# The Universal Declaration of Human Rights

**What is the Universal Declaration of Human Rights?**
The Universal Declaration of Human Rights says that all people, whoever they are and wherever they live, should be able to live safely, in freedom and peace. It has three parts: Part One is the Preamble (or introduction) which gives seven reasons for making this statement to the world; Part Two is the Proclamation in which the General Assembly of the United Nations states firmly the sense and hope of the Declaration; Part Three lists the 30 Articles or statements which are the goals of the Declaration.

**Why was it written?**
People were shocked by the effect of two world wars and, in particular, by the murder of millions of Jews by Hitler's Nazis. There was an upsurge of reaction from the whole world; people wanted to make sure that nothing like it would ever happen again. So in 1948, after three years of discussion, representatives of 48 countries (member states of the General Assembly of the United Nations) agreed upon a 'Universal Declaration of Human Rights' — not as a law, but as a statement to the whole world about how all peoples, organisations and governments should behave towards each other. It is the responsibility of every individual, and every government, to honour this Declaration in

order to safeguard freedom and justice and, therefore, the future happiness and dignity of all people. You could say that this is one of the top priorities of our time.

## Preamble

Whereas recognition of the inherent dignity and of the equal and inalienable rights of all members of the human family is the foundation of freedom, justice and peace in the world.

Whereas disregard and contempt for human rights have resulted in barbarous acts which have outraged the conscience of mankind and the advent of a world in which human beings shall enjoy freedom of speech and belief and freedom from fear and want has been proclaimed as the highest aspiration of the common people.

Whereas it is essential, if man is not to be compelled to have recourse, as a last resort, to rebellion against tyranny and oppression, that human rights should be protected by the rule of law.

Whereas the people of the United Nations have in the Charter reaffirmed their faith in fundamental human rights, in the dignity and worth of the human person and in the equal rights of men and women and have determined to promote social progress and better standards of life in larger freedom.

Whereas Member States have pledged themselves to achieve, in co-operation with the United Nations, the promotion of universal respect for and observance of human rights and fundamental freedoms.

Whereas a common understanding of these rights and freedoms is of the greatest importance for the full realisation of this pledge.

## Proclamation

Now, therefore, the General Assembly proclaims this Universal Declaration of Human Rights as a common standard of achievement for all people and all nations, to the end that every individual and every organ of society, keeping this Declaration constantly in mind, shall strive by teaching and education to promote respect for these rights and freedoms and by progressive measures, national and international, to secure their universal and effective recognition and observance, both among the peoples of Member States themselves and among the peoples of territories under their jurisdiction.

**Or to present it more simply...**

## Preamble

1. Everyone must understand that each person in the whole human family has the same rights as every other person. Until we understand this, freedom, justice and peace cannot exist.
2. The human rights of many people have been violated. Wars and other acts have oppressed people throughout history and around the world. A world in which human beings can enjoy the right to say what they think, to choose their own beliefs, and to live without fear and without want must be our greatest aim.
3. Human rights must be protected by laws.
4. All nations need to be encouraged to be friendly towards each other.
5. By this charter, the members of the United Nations state their belief in basic human rights, in the importance and value of every single person and in the equal rights of men and women. They have also agreed to work for social progress and better living standards.
6. Countries that belong to the United Nations have promised to cooperate with this international organisation in every respect so that the rights and freedoms of all people in the world should be protected and respected.
7. It is very important that all nations understand what these rights and freedoms are so that the promise can be carried out.

## Proclamation (announcement)

The General Assembly of the United Nations proclaims this Universal Declaration of Human Rights as a common standard of achievement for all peoples and all nations. Every person and every group in society is asked to work continuously to reach these goals by teaching respect for human rights and freedoms and by approving laws that will give more protection to these rights and freedoms.

## The Articles

*Article 1* All human beings are born free and equal in dignity and rights. They are endowed with reasons and conscience and should act towards one another in a spirit of brotherhood.

*Article 2* Everyone is entitled to all the rights and freedoms set forth in this Declaration, without distinction of any kind, such as race, colour, sex, language, religion, political or other opinion, national or social origin, property, birth or other status.

Furthermore, no distinction shall be made on the basis of the political, jurisdictional or international status of the country or territory to which a person belongs, whether it be independent, trust, non-self-governing or under any other limitation of sovereignty.

*Article 3* Everyone has the right to life, liberty, and security of person.

*Article 4* No one shall be held in slavery or servitude; slavery and the slave trade shall be prohibited in all their forms.

*Article 5* No one shall be subjected to torture or to cruel, inhuman or degrading treatment or punishment.

*Article 6* Everyone has the right to recognition everywhere as a person before the law.

*Article 7* All are equal before the law and are entitled without any discrimination to equal protection of the law. All are entitled to equal protection against any discrimination in violation of this Declaration and against any incitement to such discrimination.

*Article 8* Everyone has the right to an effective remedy by the competent national tribunals for acts violating the fundamental rights granted him by the constitution or by law.

*Article 9* No one shall be subjected to arbitrary arrest, detention or exile.

*Article 10* Everyone is entitled in full equality to a fair and public hearing by an independent and impartial tribunal, in the determination of his rights and obligations and of any criminal charges against him.

*Article 11* 1) Everyone charged with a penal offence has the right to be presumed innocent until proved guilty according to law in a public trial at which he has had all the guarantees necessary for his defence. 2) No one shall be held guilty of any penal offence on account of any act or omission which did not constitute a penal offence under national or international law, at the time when it was committed. Nor shall a heavier penalty be imposed than the one that was applicable at the time the penal offence was committed.

*Article 12* No one shall be subjected to arbitrary interference with his privacy, family, home or correspondence, nor to attacks upon his honour and reputation. Everyone has the right to the protection of the law against such interference or attacks.

*Article 13* 1) Everyone has the right to freedom of movement and residence within the borders of each state.

2) Everyone has the right to leave any country, including his own, and to return to his country.

*Article 14* 1) Everyone has the right to seek and to enjoy in other countries asylum from persecution.
2) This right may not be invoked in the case of prosecutions genuinely arising from non-political crimes or from acts contrary to the purposes and principles of the United Nations.

*Article 15* 1) Everyone has the right to a nationality.
2) No one shall be arbitrarily deprived of his nationality nor denied the right to change his nationality.

*Article 16* 1) Men and women of full age, without any limitation due to race, nationality or religion, have the right to marry and to found a family. They are entitled to equal rights as to marriage, during marriage and at its dissolution.
2) Marriage shall be entered into only with the free and full consent of the intending spouses.
3) The family is the natural and fundamental group unit of society and is entitled to protection by society and the State.

*Article 17* 1) Everyone has the right to own property alone as well as in association with others.
2) No one shall be arbitrarily deprived of his property.

*Article 18* Everyone has the right to freedom of thought, conscience and religion: this right includes freedom to change his religion or belief and freedom, either alone or in community with others and in public or private, to manifest his religion or belief in teaching, practice, worship and observance.

*Article 19* Everyone has the right to freedom of opinion and expression; this right includes freedom to hold opinions without interference and to seek, receive, and impart information and ideas through any media and regardless of frontiers.

*Article 20* 1) Everyone has the right to freedom of peaceful assembly and association.
2) No one may be compelled to belong to an association.

*Article 21* 1) Everyone has the right to take part in the government of his country, directly or through freely chosen representatives.
2) Everyone has the right of equal access to public service in his country.

3) The will of the people shall be the basis of the authority of government; this shall be expressed in periodic and genuine elections which shall be by universal and equal suffrage and shall be held by secret vote or by equivalent free voting procedures.

*Article 22* Everyone, as a member of society, has the right to social security and is entitled to realisation, through national effort and international co-operation and in accordance with the organisation and resources of each State, of the economic, social and cultural rights indispensable for his dignity and the free development of his personality.

*Article 23* 1) Everyone has the right to work, to free choice of employment, to just and favourable conditions of work and to protection against unemployment.
2) Everyone, without any discrimination, has the right to equal pay for equal work.
3) Everyone who works has the right to just and favourable remuneration, ensuring for himself and his family an existence worthy of human dignity, and supplemented, if necessary, by other means of social protection.
4) Everyone has the right to form and to join trade unions for the protection of his interests.

*Article 24* Everyone has the right to rest and leisure, including reasonable limitation of working hours and periodic holidays with pay.

*Article 25* 1) Everyone has the right to a standard of living adequate for the health and well-being of himself and of his family, including food, clothing, housing and medical care and necessary social services, and the right to security in the event of unemployment, disability, widowhood, old age or other lack of livelihood in circumstances beyond his control.
2) Motherhood and childhood are entitled to special care and assistance. All children, whether born in or out of wedlock, shall enjoy the same social protection.

*Article 26* 1) Everyone has the right to education. Education shall be free, at least in the elementary and fundamental stages. Elementary education shall be compulsory. Technical and professional education shall be made generally available and higher education shall be equally accessible to all on the basis of merit.

2) Education shall be directed to the full development of the human personality and to the strengthening of respect for human rights and fundamental freedoms. It shall promote understanding, tolerance and friendship among all nations, racial or religious groups, and shall further the activities of the United Nations for the maintenance of peace.
3) Parents have a prior right to choose the kind of education that shall be given to their children.

*Article 27* 1) Everyone has the right freely to participate in the cultural life of the community, to enjoy the arts and to share in scientific advancement, and its benefits.
2) Everyone has the right to the protection of the moral and material interests resulting from any scientific, literary or artistic production of which he is the author.

*Article 28* Everyone is entitled to a social and international order in which the rights and freedoms set forth in this Declaration can be fully realised.

*Article 29* 1) Everyone has duties to the community in which alone the free and full development of his personality is possible.
2) In the exercise of his rights and freedoms, everyone shall be subject only to such limitations as are determined by law solely for the purpose of securing due recognition and respect for the rights and freedoms of others and of meeting the just requirements of morality, public order and the general welfare in a democratic society.
3) These rights and freedoms may in no case be exercised contrary to the purpose and principles of the United Nations.

*Article 30* Nothing in this Declaration may be interpreted as implying for any State, group or person any right to engage in any activity or to perform any act aimed at the destruction of the rights and freedoms set forth herein.

Reproduced by permission of Amnesty International British Section

amnesty international

Pablo Picasso, gewidmet amnesty international

# The Sunlight

◆ ◆ ◆

## BY

### CHIEF DAN GEORGE

The sunlight does not leave its marks
on the grass.
So we, too, pass silently.

# Speech

## by Carlos Ferrer Salat

On behalf of the Spanish Olympic Committee, it gives me great pleasure to welcome the members of the International Olympic Committee, and leaders of sport from all over the world who have come to Barcelona to take part in this session of the IOC [International Olympic Committee] and to attend the Games of the XXV Olympiad....

As everyone knows, the Olympic Games of antiquity disappeared in 392 AD after more than 1000 years of existence. Their disappearance was not an accident. It was a logical and direct consequence of a loss of faith in the beliefs which had brought them into being and guided their development.

Humanism, which is based on a belief in human beings and their creative possibilities, their perfectibility and their striving for excellence, had been ousted by other beliefs. The complete development of the physical, spiritual and intellectual qualities of human beings was no longer fundamental. It had been set aside.

The Renaissance brought a renewed interest and belief in humanism and therefore in the physical development and character formation of men and women. It was in line with these precepts that in 1896 Baron de Coubertin revived the Games and began Olympic competition in the modern era.

Nevertheless, there are those at the present time who cast doubt on the continuity of Olympism. I wish to state here and now my absolute conviction that there is still a belief in human values and possibilities. Olympism, which is an expression of humanism and of belief in human beings, will continue to live and provide great service, not only to young people, but to the whole world, as demonstrated by the presence and interest of more than 100 countries which are taking part in the Barcelona Games. The Olympic motto *citius, altius, fortius,* "faster, higher, stronger" — in a spiritual as well as a physical sense — will retain its meaning and provide a goal for a part of humanity for a long time to come.

It is also true that the success, the great responsibility and the prominence of the Olympic Movement generate passions which are not always expressed in praise and compliments, but also in criticisms, objections, envy and jostling for power.

A speech of welcome does not provide sufficient time to deal with these questions in depth, but it does give me the opportunity to express an opinion on various aspects of the Olympic Movement which have given rise to this questioning. Firstly, the economic resources which are generated by the Games, thanks primarily to television and sponsorship, make possible an extraordinary promotion of sport throughout the world which could not take place in any other way.

Secondly, the desire for excellence and victory at all costs has, unfortunately, given rise to drug taking. And it has been the International Olympic Committee, it has been you yourselves, who bravely and at the cost of accepting great risks — as happened in Seoul — have taken a stand against this illegal practice which debases competition and can seriously damage the health of athletes.

Thirdly, thanks to their great importance and popularity, the Games have often been used for political purposes. This is true. However, it is also true that a continuous struggle has been kept up to safeguard their independence; a struggle to ensure the presence and harmonious cooperation of all the countries of the world or, to be more exact, athletes, from all the countries of the world....

I would like to express my congratulations and thanks to all these officials, members of staff, athletes and representatives of the media. The undoubted success of these Games will allow us to spread the values which we wish to promote and defend throughout the world and will be a valuable source of support for the athletes, the true heroes and heroines of this event, who we hope will be pleased with the result. I also wish to congratulate all the members and associates of the IOC on the magnificent work they have done. It has not been an easy task, there have been many difficulties, but for those of us who love sport and a challenge overcoming obstacles it is one more attraction of the task we are carrying out on behalf of not only young people, but of the whole world.

# Daily News

◆ ◆ ◆

BY

BRONWEN

WALLACE

There are days when I try to imagine the planet
pausing once in a while, like an old woman
on the edge of her bed, who sounds her bones
for the reaches her dying has made
while she slept.

These are the times when I believe
that old men do remember keener weather,
that January when their words froze in the air
or an August so blank with heat
that all it left was the smell
of the crops drying in the fields.
"It's all out of kilter now," one of them tells me,
"just more of the same all year round,"
and I want to believe the planet feels this
as a falling away she wants to tell us about
before it's too late.

Last week, a 20,000-year-old mastodon tusk
was washed up on Virginia Beach.
I believe we should take this
as a direct warning, or better still
a cry for help.

What I want most to believe, though,
is that we're all in this together.
As it is, I hardly know what to look for.
The birthrate's rising slightly, but
according to a recent survey
most teenagers can't see the point
of planning for the future.
Even my friends don't seem to feel
that what they're living these days
is a real life.

Instead, I hear men telling me
that victory is a nuclear war
which 60 million people survive.
I think they really believe this
and what's more, I'm sure it's nothing
to what they can do
whenever they want.

This is the point where I realize
how arrogant it is
to imagine the planet caring about all this.
Though I admit to the image
of a bitter woman longing for a death
that takes her whole family with her,
the mastodon tusk should be enough
to let us know
we're only another species after all.

# ACKNOWLEDGEMENTS

Care has been taken to trace ownership of copyright material contained in this text. The publishers will gladly accept any information that will enable them to rectify any reference or credit in subsequent editions.

## TEXT

**p. 1** "Space Gives Us a Global Perspective" by Wendy Warren Keebler. Reprinted with permission — The Toronto Star Syndicate. (Copyright Knight-Ridder News Service); **p. 5** "The Thread" by Tom Wayman from *In a Small House on the Outskirts of Heaven* by Tom Wayman and published by Harbour Publishing, 1989; **p. 8** "This Day in History" by Bert Almon from *Blue Sunrise* by Bert Almon (Thistledown Press, 1980) used with permission; **p. 9** "How Many Passengers on Our Planet?" by Laurence Pringle. Pages 11–17 from *Living Treasure* by Laurence Pringle. Copyright © 1991 by Laurence Pringle. By permission of Morrow Junior Books, a division of William Morrow & Company, Inc.; **p. 12** "Inherit the Earth" by Lynn Moore. *The Gazette*, Montreal; **pp. 17–19** "Data Bank," "What A Waste," "A 10-Point Plan," "Just How Committed Are We?" by Rupert J. Taylor. Reprinted with the permission of *Canada and the World* magazine, Oakville, Ontario; **p. 21** "Memo to the 21st Century" by Philip Appleman from *Open Doorways: Poems by Philip Appleman*, published in 1976 by W.W. Norton & Company, Inc.; **p. 23** "Requiem for a River" by Kim Williams. Courtesy of The Wilderness Society; **p. 24** "Digging In" by Elizabeth Brewster is reprinted from *Digging In* by permission of Oberon Press; **p. 26** "National Totems" by David Day (pp.108–118) from *Noah's Choice* by David Day (Viking, 1990, Puffin Books, 1991), Copyright © David Day, 1990. Reproduced by permission of Penguin Books Ltd.; **p. 34** "Drawing the Line in the Vanishing Jungle" by David M. Schwartz. Copyright 1991 National Wildlife Federation from the July/August issue of *International Wildlife*; **p. 42** "A Poem for the Rainforest" by Judith Nicholls © Judith Nicholls 1987. From *Midnight Forest* by Judith Nicholls published by Faber & Faber and reprinted by permission of the author; **p. 44** "The Fragile Land" by Janice Hamilton. Reprinted with the permission of *Canada and the World* magazine, Oakville, Ontario; **p. 47** "Incredible Inedible Pie" by Robert Priest is reprinted from *Do Whales Jump at Night?* (Groundwood Books), © Robert Priest; **p. 48** "Beggarman" by Susan Shwartz originally appeared in *2041* edited by Jane Yolen; **p. 70** "Rich Man, Poor Man" From *African Folktales* by Roger D. Abrahams. Copyright © 1983 by Roger D. Abrahams. Reprinted by permission of Pantheon Books, a division of Random House, Inc.; **p. 72** "Project Report" by John Coutts. From *Act Justly* © 1987 CAFOD and Christian Aid. Reprinted by permission of Collins Liturgical, an imprint of HarperCollins Publishers Limited; **p. 74** "People From Mars" by Helena Norberg-Hodge. From *Ancient Futures: Learning from Ladakh* by Helena Norberg-Hodge. Copyright © 1991 by Helena Norberg-Hodge. Reprinted with permission from Sierra Club Books; **p. 79** "The Law of the Market-Place" by Sibani Raychaudhuri. This extract is from *Right of Way* by the Asian Women Writers' Workshop first published by The Women's Press Ltd., 1988, 34 Great Sutton Street, London, EC1V ODX; **p. 81** "Holy Cow" by Sehdev Kumar. From *The Globe and Mail*, June 4, 1992. Reprinted by permission of the author, Sehdev Kumar; **p. 84**

"Village People" by Bessie Head. Permission is granted by John Johnson Ltd., London, on behalf of the Estate of the Author; **p. 89** "Hunger" by Laurence Binyon. With the permission of Mrs. Nicolete Gray and The Society of Authors on behalf of the Laurence Binyon Estate; **p. 90** "The Unofficial Ambassadors" by Debra Black. Reprinted with permission — The Toronto Star Syndicate; **p. 96** "The Third World" by Ian Keeling. From June '91 of *TG Magazine...Voices of Today's Generation*, 202 Cleveland St., Toronto, Ontario M4S 2W6 (416) 487-3204; **p. 100** "Zack's Notebook" by Sarah Pirtle from *An Outbreak of Peace* by Sarah Pirtle. Reprinted with permission from New Society Publishers; **p. 111** "In the Next War" by Robert Priest is reprinted from *Scream Blue Living* (The Mercury Press, 1992), © Robert Priest; **p. 112** "Mending Wall" by Robert Frost from *The Poetry of Robert Frost* edited by Edward Connery Lathem, 1969, and published by Henry Holt and Co., Inc.; **p. 114** "Print Your Name Large" by Joan Finnigan from *More Than Words Can Say*. Reprinted by permission from the author; **p. 118** "Literacy Program Gives New Hope and Pleasure to Family's Life" by Florence Loyie. Reprinted with permission of *The Edmonton Journal*; **p. 120** and **p. 122** "Why Don't They Have Shelter?", "The Shelter Checklist," "Street Numbers" from *No Place Like Home: The Global Shelter Crisis*, Development Education Department, World Vision Canada, 1991. Used by permission; **p. 122** "It Came From the Swamp." Excerpted and adapted from "Changing My Shantytown," from *Under the Same Sun*, Fall 1989, Canadian International Development Agency. Reprinted with permission from World Vision Canada. **p. 124** "Child Labor Aids 'Miracle' of Asia" by Dave Todd, Southam News; **p. 126** "Trying Not to See" by Cathy Beveridge. Reprinted by permission of the author; **p. 131** "The Rebellion of the Magical Rabbits" by Ariel Dorfman © 1987 by Ariel Dorfman, reprinted with permission of Wylie, Aitken & Stone, Inc.; **p. 141** "The Universal Declaration of Human Rights." Reproduced by permission of Amnesty International British Section; **p. 149** "The Sunlight" by Chief Dan George. Excerpt from *My Heart Soars* by Chief Dan George. Reprinted by permission of Hancock House Publishers Ltd.; **p. 150** "Speech" by Mr. Carlos Ferrer Salat. Reprinted from the *Olympic Review*; **p. 152** "Daily News" by Bronwen Wallace is reprinted from *Common Magic* by permission of Oberon Press.

## PHOTOGRAPHS
**p. 4** NASA 90-HC-98; **pp. 16, 20, 28** World Wildlife Fund; **pp. 35, 38, 41** © Victor Englebert 1990; **p. 56** Michael Buller; **p. 69** UNICEF/Stephenie Hollyman; **p. 83** World Wildlife Fund; **p. 88** UNICEF/Jorgen Schytte; **p. 97** and **p. 98** Mir Lada/TG Magazine; **p. 115** UNICEF/Stephenie Hollyman; (inset) UNICEF/Sean Sprague; **p. 117** UNICEF/D. Mangurian; **p. 148** Amnesty International.